Thermodynamics and the Development of Order

Emmett L. Williams, *Editor*

Creation Research Society
Monograph Series: No. 1

D1599908

Creation Research Society Books

Thermodynamics and the Development of Order
Edited by Emmett L. Williams
Illustrations by Robert W. Martin
Cover Design by Joe Whitaker

ISBN: 0-940384-01-9

Printed in the United States of America

Preface

Recognizing the need to publish technical monographs on various topics of interest to creationists, the Board of Directors of the Creation Research Society asked George Mulfinger to direct such a project. Mr. Mulfinger then asked me to edit a monograph on thermodynamics. Of the eight creationist scientists invited to write chapters, six men responded with contributions to the volume. Their willingness to devote their time and effort to this undertaking is deeply appreciated.

George Mulfinger, M.S. with degrees in chemistry and physics, has an interest in the history of science and has written many biographies of Christian men of science. Mr. Mulfinger graciously consented to write a brief history of the laws of thermodynamics.

Harold Armstrong, M.S., editor of the Creation Research Society Quarterly, has published several articles in the journal on thermodynamic subjects. His discussions on the definition of order have been particularly helpful and in this vein his essay on order, uniformity, and arrangement is particularly welcome.

David Boylan, Ph.D. in chemical engineering, has made contributions to the Quarterly employing unique open system thermodynamic arguments. In his chapter he points out the necessity of a Creator to explain the presence of order in the universe.

Duane Gish, Ph.D., is well known for his successful debates against evolutionary scientists and his penetrating writings on the origin of life. His thorough treatment of the latter subject is an excellent addition to this volume.

Ralph Ancil, B.A., offers a creationist interpretation of genetics using thermodynamic principles. He suggests a new discipline in which to reinterpret scientific data.

Henry M. Morris, Ph.D., has written a far-reaching philosophical chapter for the monograph. In his usual excellent style Dr. Morris offers physical as well as spiritual conclusions based on the universal natural processes of conservation and degeneration.

The editor has attempted to complement the aforementioned writings with some of his articles previously published in the Quarterly. Where required, necessary revisions were made.

The selections range from highly technical material to the more readable popularizations. Hopefully, there is something in the monograph for the scientist as well as the serious layman in this field of very fruitful creationist effort.

Emmett L. Williams, Ph.D.
Norcross, Georgia

63537

Contents

I. Introduction

1

HISTORY OF THERMODYNAMICS
George Mulfinger, Jr.

Introduction

A penetrating and comprehensive treatment of the history of thermodynamics would require a treatise almost as extensive as one dealing with the history of science. To keep this portion of the monograph within reasonable bounds, it will be necessary to skim just a few of the high points. I have arbitrarily chosen to restrict the discussion to the four *laws* of thermodynamics, since at least two of these are of special interest to creationists. The reader should be aware, however, that the science of thermodynamics extends far beyond the confines of the four laws themselves. The discussion is, for the most part, chronological. In following this order of events, however, the numbering of the laws will be somewhat out of sequence, since the so-called "zeroth law" was not formulated until the 20th century.

The First Law

The first law of thermodynamics, which states that energy can be neither created nor destroyed, is a remarkably broad scientific generalization. It asserts that *all* types of energy—heat, mechanical, chemical, electrical, etc.—are quantitatively conserved in conversions from one kind to another. Such a sweeping generalization did not come about in a single stroke, but was, rather, the combined result of meticulous observations on a number of separate types of energy conversions.

Historically, the conservation of mechanical energy was the first such principle to be suggested. Christian Huygens (1629-1695) in 1668 stated that the quantity mv^2 is conserved in elastic collisions. Though this quantity is double the familiar $\frac{1}{2}mv^2$, the principle he enunciated was essentially conservation of kinetic energy. At about this same time Newton and others were becoming aware of the conservative nature of conversions between kinetic and potential energy, kinetic energy and work, and potential energy and work.

Efforts leading to an understanding of the quantitative connection between mechanical energy and heat suffered a more difficult history. Though Francis Bacon, Robert Boyle, and Robert Hooke had previously deduced that heat is a property of a body arising from the motion of its parts, the 18th century had brought a widespread preoccupation with the caloric theory—an erroneous view that heat was a fluid that flowed from hot bodies to cold bodies. Such notables as Joseph Black, the discoverer of carbon dioxide, endorsed the theory enthusiastically, and Lavoisier, the chemist who disproved the phlogiston theory, preferred not to take a stand on which was superior—the caloric theory or the kinetic theory. Interestingly, the properties postulated for "caloric" led to a "conservation of heat" principle. Since caloric was a substance that could be neither created nor destroyed, its quantity in nature had to be conserved.

The first hint that all was not well with this theory came with the famous "cannon-boring experiment" conducted by Count Rumford (Benjamin Thompson, 1753-1814). According to the caloric theory, the amount of heat produced in drilling a metal should be proportional to the volume of the material removed, since the "caloric" supposedly resided between the ultimate particles of the metal and was released when the particles were separated. But Rumford observed no correlation whatever between the volume removed and the heat produced. On the contrary he observed that some of the most copious heat production occurred when a dull drill was used and a minimal amount of metal was cut. A seemingly unlimited supply of heat could be produced under such conditions. In a report to the Royal Society in 1798 he theorized that heat was the result of motion in the ultimate particles of the metal. Humphrey Davy (1778-1829) continued this line of attack on the caloric theory in the early 1800's, but several decades were yet to elapse before the final demise of the theory.

James Prescott Joule (1818-1889), a Manchester brewer, envisioned a more comprehensive principle than one dealing solely with heat, or solely with mechanical energy. Accordingly, he began a series of experiments in 1840 designed to unite heat and mechanical energy under a single law. Before he was able to publish his results, however, Julius Robert Mayer (1814-1878), a young German physician, published a paper in 1842 enunciating a general conservation of energy principle. The paper, entitled "Remarks on the Forces of Inorganic Nature," appeared in Justus von Liebig's journal *Annalen der Chemie und Pharmacie*. The paper was largely philosophical rather than empirical, but in it Mayer's keen scientific intuition was much in evidence. He perceived that energy is indestructible, quantitatively convertible, and imponderable (weightless). In addition, he offered a reasonable explanation for the difference between the constant-volume and constant-pressure heat capacities of gases, showing that the latter situation required an additional amount of heat to perform work.

Joule's first results, published in 1843, described a contrivance in which falling weights turned an electric generator, which in turn heated

2

water by means of a resistance wire. For 13 separate measurements he reported that it required an average of 838 foot-pounds of work to raise the temperature of a pound of water one degree Fahrenheit. In other words, 838 foot-pounds of work were required to develop one Btu of heat. The value of this quantity, which is called the "mechanical equivalent of heat," varied somewhat from experiment to experiment because of frictional losses and other effects, but the values obtained were close enough to lend confidence to the view that the discrepancies could be resolved by increasing refinement of technique. Later he used an arrangement in which the falling weights were connected directly to a brass paddle wheel in the water.

In subsequent experiments, he reported 770 ft-lb for heating water with a perforated piston, 795 ft-lb for the temperature drop of rapidly expanding air, and 774 ft-lb for experiments involving the motion of water through narrow tubes. By 1850 he had settled on a value of 772 ft-lb. The currently accepted value is 778.26 ft-lb.

An important outcome of Joule's work, in addition to his own enunciation of a unified conservation of energy principle, was a definitive refutation of the caloric theory. In a lecture delivered in Manchester in 1847 he administered the coup-de-grace to that already infirm and dying theory by showing that, inasmuch as heat could be converted to kinetic or potential energy, it could not possibly be a material substance. He explained the source of the heating in Rumford's experiment simply as a conversion from mechanical energy to heat energy. The elusive "caloric principle" had finally been banished from science once and for all.

Some insight into Joule's scientific philosophy can be learned from the following quotes taken from two different stages of his work. (See A. B. Arons, *Development of Concepts of Physics*, Addison-Wesley Publ. Co., 1965, pp. 416, 429.)

1843: "I shall lose no time in repeating and extending these experiments, being satisfied that the grand agents of nature are, by the Creator's fiat, *indestructible*; and that wherever mechanical force is expended (work is dissipated), an exact equivalent of heat is *always* obtained."

1847: "When we consider our own frames,'fearfully and wonderfully made,' we observe in the motion of our limbs a continual conversion of heat into living force (kinetic energy), which may be either converted back again into heat or employed in producing an attraction through space (potential energy), as when a man ascends a mountain. Indeed the phenomena of nature, whether mechanical, chemical or vital, consist almost entirely in a continual conversion of attraction through space, living force, and heat into one another. Thus it is that order is maintained in the universe—nothing is deranged, nothing ever lost, but the entire machinery, complicated as it is, works smoothly and harmoniously. And though, as in the awful vision of Ezekiel, 'wheel may be in middle of wheel,' and every thing may appear complicated and involved in the apparent confusion and intricacy of an almost endless variety of causes, effects, conversions, and arrangements, yet is the most perfect regularity preserved.''

One more 19th century luminary should be mentioned at this point. Hermann von Helmholtz (1821-1894), a young German physicist and physiologist, extended the range of conservation of energy calculations to include a number of simple electrical, magnetic, and chemical phenomena. The results of this work were published in 1847, along with his own formulation of a general conservation of energy principle.

The first law has given an excellent account of itself not only in experimental tests of its veracity, but also in serving as a foundation for developing a quantitative understanding of many different branches of physics. The atomic age has brought its extension to still one more type of energy conversion. *Mass* is now treated as a form of energy having a quantity equal to mc^2. Whereas it might appear that energy is being "created" in a nuclear explosion, in actuality the process is simply an energy conversion from mass to heat, light, and other more traditional forms of energy. The reverse type of occurrence, in which mass is produced from other forms of energy, has been observed in such processes as pair production. Thus, what at first might have appeared to be an exception to the first law has been recognized as just one more confirmation of its correctness.

The Second Law
The first law specified nothing about the direction in which natural processes occurred. Another law was needed if this aspect of nature was to be described. It had long been noted that some things happen with ease in nature while other things never happen at all. For example, heat always flows from a hot body to a cold body, never the reverse. A gas always tends to expand and occupy a larger volume, never contract into a smaller volume. Of course, outside energy could be invoked to bring about the reversal of such a process, but then it would no longer be a *natural* process. Although there had been an abundance of observations of such preferred directionality of "one-wayness" in nature, no one had succeeded in comprehending it under a unifying law.

4

In 1824 Sadi Carnot (1796-1832), a French physicist, had pointed out that every heat engine requires a hot body or source of heat, and a cold body or sink, and that as the engine operates, heat passes from the source to the sink. He analyzed the simplest idealized heat engine that could be envisioned—one that was perfectly frictionless and that permitted no loss of heat by conduction. His analysis of such an engine (called a "Carnot engine") as it goes through one complete cycle of operation, is a veritable cornerstone of thermodynamics. Carnot's findings furnished one more example of the "one-wayness" of nature. In such an engine only a portion of the heat from the source can be utilized to do useful work. The rest must be expelled to the sink and wasted. There is no way that any scientist or engineer, however clever, can turn the lost heat around and force it to perform useful work. One writer has likened this lost heat to a "tax" that must be paid on the heat that is utilized. If the situation is this unfavorable for an *idealized* engine, how much less favorable must be the lot of a real-life engine that *does* have friction in its parts and *does* have heat losses by conduction.

Carnot's treatment of heat cycles was cast into its modern form by Rudolph Clausius (1822-1888) and Lord Kelvin (William Thomson, 1824-1907) a German and an Irish physicist, respectively. This was greatly facilitated by Kelvin's invention of a thermodynamic temperature scale, the first scale on which the number "zero" actually signified the *absolute* zero of temperature. Kelvin pondered the question of "one-wayness" in nature for many months. Finally, in the early part of 1852, he was able to formulate one of the most important generalizations in all of science. In a paper entitled "On a Universal Tendency in Nature to the Dissipation of Mechanical Energy" he set forth the following three propositions. (See Silvanus P. Thompson, *Life of Lord Kelvin,* Macmillan and Co., London, 1910, pp. 290, 291.)

1. There is at present in the material world a universal tendency to the dissipation of mechanical energy.
2. Any restoration of mechanical energy, without more than an equivalent of dissipation, is impossible in inanimate material processes, and is probably never effected by means of organized matter, either endowed with vegetable life or subjected to the will of an animated creature.
3. Within a finite period of time past, the earth must have been, and within a finite period of time to come the earth must again be, unfit for the habitation of man as at present constituted, unless operations have been or are to be performed which are impossible under the laws to which the known operations going on at present in the material world are subject.

This, then, is the original statement of the second law of thermodynamics. Though energy is conserved, it is becoming less available. It is, to use Kelvin's terminology, "irrevocably lost to man and therefore 'wasted,' though not annihilated." (See S. P. Thompson, p. 288.) The implications of the second law are momentous, and Kelvin's keen scientific insight enabled him to perceive many far-reaching truths from its inception. In his third proposition, quoted above, is implicit the recognition of the fact that the second law presents an impassible barrier to the evolution of the earth. In other papers and letters, as well as in his lectures, he made it perfectly clear that he was a staunch foe of Darwinism and any theory of spontaneous generation. Though a Bible-believing Christian, he supported these views with scientific arguments rather than Scripture. Kelvin was also fully aware of the implication of the second law that the universe is running down, and he pointed out how the second law militated against the possibility of perpetual motion.

Another form of the second law was enunciated by Clausius in 1854: "Heat cannot of itself, without the intervention of any external agency, pass from a colder to a hotter body." (See S. Glasstone, *Textbook of Physical Chemistry,* D. Van Nostrand Co., New York, 1946, p. 217.) Clausius also defined a quantity called *entropy*, the energy per degree of absolute temperature that cannot be recovered as work. He was then able to give the following very succinct statement of the first and second laws:

First Law: The total amount of energy in nature is constant.

Second Law: The total amount of entropy in nature is increasing.

Ludwig Boltzmann (1844-1906), an Austrian physicist, recognizing that a disordered state is more probable than one of complete order, tied together entropy and probability by defining a *thermodynamic probability* in 1896. Subsequently, in 1912, Max Planck (1858-1947) published the justification for the equation that has become the basis for modern statistical thermodynamics.

The Third Law

Planck's famous paper of 1912 suggested that the entropy of pure solids and liquds should approach zero at the absolute zero of temperature. This generalization has been found to hold for solids but not necessarily for liquids. The law is therefore now stated in the following form: "Every substance has a finite positive entropy, but at the absolute zero of temperature the entropy may become zero, and does so become in the case of a perfect crystalline substance." (See Glasstone, p. 865.) Important contributions leading to this understanding came from T. W. Richards in 1902 and Walter Nernst in 1906 (the Nernst heat theorem). Using the third law it has become possible to calculate absolute entropies for many substances, not only of solids but also of materials that are liquid or gaseous at room temperature.

The Zeroth Law

Curiously, the zeroth law of thermodynamics, which is the most basic of the four, was the last to make its appearance. Stating that "two systems in thermal equilibrium with a third system are in thermal equilibrium with each other," the law was first formulated by R. H. Fowler in 1931. Because it precedes the first and second laws conceptually, it was deemed appropriate to give it a lower number than either of those laws.

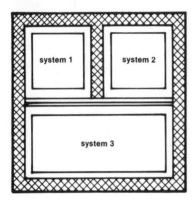 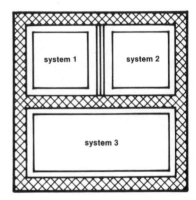

Figure 1 The zeroth law of thermodynamics

The zeroth law seems eminently logical from an intuitive standpoint. In Figure 1(a), systems 1 and 2 are both thermally coupled to system 3, but insulated from each other. If, under these conditions, no heat passes between systems 1 and 3, or 2 and 3, then no heat will pass between systems 1 and 2 when the thermal barrier between them is removed (Figure 1b).

The zeroth law can be extended to assert that all systems in thermal equilibrium with each other share a common property. That property, which we experience as "hotness" or "coldness," is none other than temperature.

Conclusions

It is probably no exaggeration to claim that the laws of thermodynamics represent some of the best science we have today. While the utterances from authorities in some fields (such as astronomy) seem to change almost daily, the science of thermodynamics has been noteworthy for its stability. In many decades of careful observations, not a single departure from any of these laws has ever been noted. If we as creationists were forced to choose a single most reliable branch of science to use in buttressing our position, the science of thermodynamics would be a good choice indeed.

2

Thermodynamics and Evolution: A Creationist View

Emmett L. Williams

What is Thermodynamics?

Consider the word thermodynamics. Thermo- is a combining form from the Greek word therme- (heat). Dynamic comes from the Greek word dynamis (power). Thus, thermodynamics is the study of heat power. The subject of thermodynamics arose historically from the study of heat engines, and the problems involved in converting heat into mechanical work.[1] One may legitimately ask how the study of heat movement can be related to the theory of evolution? This question must and can be answered.

But an even more basic question must be answered first: what is heat? Heat is a form of energy, but more importantly, it is a form of energy in transition-heat flow.[2] The idea of movement is very important, since heat can be detected only if it moves from its source. Therefore, heat is the name for energy as it is transferred from one region to another by the thermal processes of conduction, convection, and radiation.[3]

There are other related forms of energy besides heat, such as mechanical, electrical, and magnetic energy which can be transformed by various means. Heat may be transformed into mechanical work, or into electrical energy, and vice versa. James Joule (1818-1889) was the first scientist to show quantitatively the mechanical equivalence of heat. The relation he established may be written mathematically as follows:

$$W = JQ \qquad (1)$$

where W = mechanical work dissipated, Q = quantity of heat produced (by mechanical work), and J = proportionality constant.

The study of thermodynamics is actually broader. It involves the movement of energy, and the conversion of one form of energy into another, and particularly involves relations between heat and work.[4] Thus thermodynamics can serve as a field of unification for all of the exact sciences,[5] since energy is required for all natural processes.

Another question of importance is related to this discussion: what is energy? Energy is the ability to do work. Lord Kelvin gave a more sophisticated definition:

> The energy of a material system is the sum, expressed in mechanical units of work, of all the effects which are pro-

duced outside the system when the system is made to pass in any manner from the state in which it happens to be to a certain arbitrarily fixed initial (standard) state.[6] In the first definition, a system that is more energetic can do more work than another. In the second definition, there is no such quantity as absolute energy, but only relative energy; only energy differences can be measured.

Relation of Thermodynamics to Evolution

Back to the original question: how can thermodynamics be related to evolution? Consider the definition of evolution given by Sir Julian Huxley, the British biologist:

> Evolution in the extended sense can be defined as a directional and essentially irreversible process occurring in time, which in its course gives rise to an increase of variety and an increasingly high level of organization in its products. Our present knowledge indeed forces us to the view that the whole of reality is evolution-a single process of self-transformation.[7]

Or as Sidney Fox states:

> Evolution, however, has put together the smallest components; it has proceeded from the simple to the complex.[8]

Obviously evolution involves transformation, and natural transformations require energy. Such a description of evolution as given above would require tremendous quantities of energy and many energy transformations. The process of evolution requires energy in various forms, and thermodynamics is the study of energy movement and transformation. The two fields are clearly related. Scientific laws that govern thermodynamics must also govern evolution.

Thermodynamic Systems

Methods of thermodynamics may be applied to a particular system under investigation. A moving automobile, a working person, a pot of water, a beaker of acid, a piece of metal, or a cylinder of gas may be treated as a thermodynamic system. All chemical reactions, physical processes, and natural operations may be treated as systems under study.

A system is some part of the physical universe "isolated" from its immediate environment so that it can be studied. An imaginary boundary is placed around the system to separate it from its surroundings. For practical purposes, the rest of the universe may be ignored, as being independent of local happenings in the system and its immediate surroundings.[9] (See Figure 1)

10

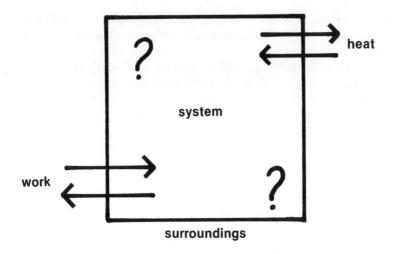

Figure 1   Representation of work and heat passing through a
system boundary

The system is a reservoir of energy no matter what it is, or how complicated it is. A moving automobile, a piece of hot or cold metal, a pot of frozen or boiling water, a reacting mixture of chemicals, or a college sophomore may all be considered as reservoirs of energy from the standpoint of thermodynamics. This generality is what makes the application of thermodynamic principles universal. The application of other scientific methods may cause the investigator to become lost in endless details of atomic structure and mechanistic rationalizations, in which logical difficulties appear, leaving the theory incomplete.

Many unnecessary scientific details may be avoided in investigating thermodynamic systems, when thought of as reservoirs of energy. A scientist need only measure a few easily determined properties (or variables) of a system to calculate its relative energy content. Such properties as temperature, pressure, volume, and composition often provide all the information needed to completely define a thermodynamic system. This approach is very simple. Interactions involving various energy exchanges between the system and its immediate surroundings can be followed easily.

First Law of Thermodynamics
Robert Mayer (1814-1878) was the first scientist to suggest the general principle of energy conservation. Mass and energy can be transformed one to another, but the total energy content of the universe remains the same. There is no destruction or creation of matter or energy now going on in the physical universe. This was considered a bold and

speculative idea in 1842.[10] Basically the conservation of energy principle is the first law of thermodynamics. In Mayer's own words, this law is stated:

> I therefore hope that I may reckon on the reader's assent when I lay down as an axiomatic truth that, just as in the case of matter, so also in the case of force (the then current term for energy), only a transformation but never a creation takes place.[11] (Parentheses added)

The first law has universal application and there are no known exceptions within the limits of experimental error.

It should be obvious to anyone, who believes in creation by direct acts of God, that only He can create something out of nothing. Man is incapable of such creation. Once God stopped creating, conservation processes began. (One other consideration, degeneration, will be covered later.) Man can only utilize what has been created; he can transform various created quantities, but never create something without using existing material.

If the energy of the universe is conserved, it now becomes the scientist's job to keep up with the energy moving in and out of a system. He can do this very simply because energy transfers usually can be placed into two categories: heat and work.

Equation for First Law

A system can receive or reject heat depending upon the temperature of the immediate surroundings. Temperature is an arbitrary measure of the thermal energy of a system. If the surroundings are hotter (higher temperature) than the system, thermal energy will flow into the system, and if the surroundings are colder (lower temperature) than the system, thermal energy will flow out of the system.

Secondly, a system can do work or have work done on it. For instance, an enclosed gas system can expand (it does work on its immediate surroundings), or be compressed (surroundings do work on the gas). The work done on or by the system can be mechanical, electrical, magnetic, etc.

A simple mathematical statement of the first law to account for all of these changes for a given system is:

$$dU = dQ + dW \qquad (2)$$

where d is a mathematical term* which can be interpreted as "the change in" or "difference in"; U represents the energy of a system, normally expressed as internal energy; Q = heat content of system; and W = work done on or by system.

*To completely understand the expression, a knowledge of calculus is required.

12

In this equation the change in internal energy of a system (dU) is equal to the change in heat content of a system (dQ) plus the work done on or by the system (dW). If the system gains heat energy, dQ is positive; if it loses heat, dQ is negative. For work done on the system, dW is positive, and for work done by the system on its surroundings, dW is negative. Only energy differences can be measured.

An interesting comment on internal energy is made by King:

> No simple monosyllabic word exists as a name for the energy which we have represented by U. Perhaps the Anglo-Saxon word sawl, meaning the spirit or essence of a substance is suitable. Than sawl, like work and heat, is one form of energy during its transfer between a system and the near-surround.[12]

From a Scriptural viewpoint, Hebrews 1:2 states that the Lord is "upholding all things by the word of his power." How is the creation being conserved, or what is the source of this energy? Morris,[13] on the authority of this verse, states that it is the Creator Himself.

The First Law and Evolution

The first law of thermodynamics indicates that creation is finished. Only processes of conservation, preservation, and maintenance are scientifically possible. Refer again to Huxley's definition of evolution. Evolution is irreversible in time and is continuing. Evolution gives rise to new products, in other words, creation processes are supposed to be in progress now. Obviously the first law of thermodynamics, and evolution cannot both be true.

What is the "best" science, the first law or evolution? The first law is primarily an empirical law. Equation 2, given above, was developed through experimentation. Granted, Mayer suggested the principle of energy conservation a priori, as far as modern science is concerned, and Helmholtz presented the precise mathematical formulation in 1847. Yet, the first law is backed solidly by experience and experimentation. Direct observation of the way matter behaves demonstrates that the first law is true.

What about the validity of the theory of evolution? The very use of the term "theory" should suggest that it is not scientific law. Is evolution backed by experience and experimentation? Is it directly observable? No! Neither Huxley, nor any other scientist can prove that the process which he defines has taken place or is taking place. The obvious conclusion is that the first law of thermodynamics is science, and the theory of evolution is not.

Someone may wish to side-step the direct confrontation of the first law of thermodynamics and the theory of evolution. Someone may reason that the first law simply says that energy and matter are not being created or destroyed at this time. However, could not the existing energy and matter be used to develop new products, greater variety, and more organization? Suppose that new matter and energy are not being created; they are only being used in an evolutionary process.

To answer this hypothesis, we must understand the direction of natural processes. As natural processes occur, which way do they tend to drift-toward evolutionary development, in an opposite direction, or in neither direction? The second law of thermodynamics gives the answer to this question.

Second Law of Thermodynamics

When men began work with heat engines in the last century, the second law of thermodynamics was formulated. Most modern industries obtain power from heat engines. For instance, coal or oil is burned to produce steam which produces electrical power which in turn is used by machines in industrial plants to produce mechanical work. Basically, heat energy is converted into mechanical work.

Heat transfer is of prime importance for such operations. The first thing that can be noted in heat transfer is that heat will flow only one way. Heat will flow only from a body of higher temperature to a body of lower temperature.

For example, if a hot iron ball is placed beside a cold iron ball, no heat energy will be transferred from the cold ball to the hot ball, resulting in a decrease of temperature of the cold ball while the hot ball increases in temperature. What happens is that the hot ball begins to lose heat energy, whereas the cold ball receives this heat energy until both balls come to the same temperature.

Why will heat not go from a cold body to a hot body? It is simply because of the character of the physical universe. This direction of heat flow has always been observed. This is the direction of a particular natural process (heat flow). One statement of the second law is that heat cannot pass spontaneously from a body of lower temperature to a body of higher temperature.[14] The conventional second law of thermodynamics was introduced by Clausius (1850) and Kelvin (1851), independently. Carnot (1824) actually discovered the essence of the second law before it was stated in this form.[15]

Interestingly, all natural processes tend to go spontaneously only one way. King says:

This "onewayness" appears to be a very fundamental

characteristic of natural processes. The second law of thermodynamics epitomizes our experiences with respect to the direction taken by thermophysical processes.[16] In the definition of the second law, spontaneous refers to the process as unrestrained. In other words, the process is allowed to proceed naturally without any external restraints. Any natural process is a spontaneously occurring one.

Consider again heat transfer: the flow goes from a reservoir of high temperature to a reservoir of low temperature. As the heat energy moves from the hot reservoir to the cold reservoir, there is heat lost to the surroundings. The process of heat transfer is not 100% efficient. The first law of thermodynamics has been obeyed. The energy that is lost to the surroundings is not destroyed; it simply becomes unavailable to do any useful work.

Suppose heat energy is being used to produce mechanical work. If 1000 calories of heat energy are generated at the source, after the energy conversion is accomplished, the final machine may be able to produce only 300 calories of mechanical work. (See Figure 2) Thus there is an unavoidable waste of heat.

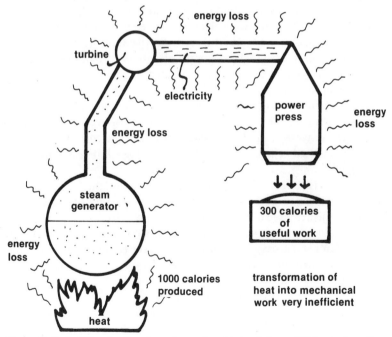

Figure 2   Only 300 calories of work can be obtained from 1000 calories of heat

15

Clausius in 1865 introduced the concept of entropy in connection with this heat waste.[17] High entropy heat would have considerable waste, whereas low entropy heat would have very little waste. In fact the entropy of the heat is more important than the amount of the heat.[18] It is not only of interest to provide heat to produce mechanical work, but also the temperature at which the heat is produced becomes important in determining how much of the heat can be utilized later for mechanical work. Heat produced at one temperature will have a different entropy (useability) value than heat produced at another temperature.

Another Statement of Second Law

This inefficiency of thermal operations led to another statement of the second law. It is impossible to build an engine which would extract heat from a given source and transform it into mechanical energy without bringing about some additional changes in the systems taking part.[19] This statement eliminates the possibility of any perpetual-motion engine.

Although this statement refers to thermal processes, it has been found through observation and experimentation that the second law applies to all natural processes. Natural processes are inefficient. There is a waste of energy in any natural process. All energy being utilized has an entropy value or has the property of entropy. As more and more energy is utilized, more energy is wasted, and the entropy of the universe increases.

Clausius summarized the two laws of thermodynamics by saying that the total energy of the universe is a constant, and the total entropy content of the universe increases.[20] This means that the energy wasted can never be utilized again. It becomes unavailable, but it has not been destroyed.

All natural processes occur in a direction such that there is an increase in entropy. The second law shows the direction of natural processes. Consider the example of the hot and cold iron balls. The hot one cools and the cold one heats up until they reach a common temperature. If this new temperature is greater or lower than the room in which the balls are located, then the temperature of the balls will change until it equals the room temperature. The balls gain or lose heat energy until they reach the temperature of their environment.

It is known from thermodynamics that all isolated systems proceed toward a state of equilibrium; i.e., a system changes its state toward one in which the physical properties of the system are as uniform throughout as possible under the prevailing conditions.[21] If the system is exposed to its surroundings, both the system and surroundings will approach a state of equilibrium with each other. Natural processes proceed so that entropy increases, a movement toward the state of equilibrium which is one of maximum entropy.

Natural Processes Occur Spontaneously

All natural processes occur spontaneously. It is possible to force some processes in a reverse direction; however, once the system is released from this force, it will proceed spontaneously in the natural direction toward equilibrium.

For instance, a beaker of alcohol and water will mix spontaneously. As long as the mixture stays in a beaker it will not tend to unmix spontaneously. By subjecting the mixture to thermal or chemical operations the two could be separated, but never will they separate by themselves. The mixture of alcohol and water is a disordered arrangement of alcohol and water molecules. The two separate beakers of alcohol and water are not as disordered as the mixture. Thus, natural processes tend toward a state of higher entropy (a state of higher disorder). (See Figure 3)

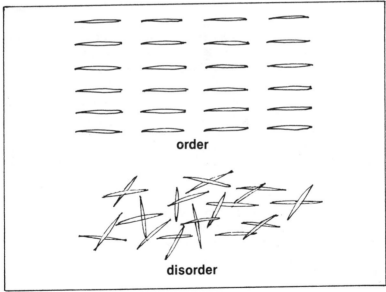

order

disorder

Figure 3 Order versus disorder

The equilibrium state of a system is the state of maximum disorder. Therefore entropy is associated with disorder. To explore fully the concept of entropy and disorder, statistical mechanics must be introduced

17

and this is beyond the scope of this discussion. For a more complete discussion of entropy and disorder, see reference 22.

The principle of increasing entropy in thermodynamics is true of an isolated system. This principle is of extremely general application because all material, that is in any way affected by a process, may be included within a single isolated system.[23]

Caratheodory established in 1909 a rigorous mathematical basis for the concept of entropy. Since he deduced the existence of entropy as a solution function for a particular differential equation, he showed that entropy must be due to some very special character of the world in which we live.[24] A state of maximum entropy in the universe would be one of uniform temperature. This could only be attained when all of the high energy sources have dissipated their energy.

As bodies, such as the sun, dissipate their energy, there is a tremendous waste of energy. The high energy (high temperature) bodies cannot receive energy from the lower energy (low temperature) bodies to replenish their supply so they are wearing out (even though the process is very slow). The universe is "running down" from a standpoint of available energy for natural processes. If such a state of uniform temperature ever occurred, it would be a state of maximum disorder and maximum entropy.

All aging or wearing out processes are toward a state of maximum entropy. Consider an article of clothing. As it is worn, it fades and becomes threadbare. The original garment represents a state of low entropy compared to the final worn-out garment. Much energy was expended to take the cotton or wool from its original form until it was formed into a completed garment. As this energy was utilized, much energy waste occurred, increasing the entropy of the universe. The cotton or wool fibers did not spontaneously form a dress; they were mechanically formed and chemically treated and forced into the article of clothing.

As the garment deteriorates, it is increasing in entropy. No matter how the garment is cleaned and restored, it never can maintain its "newness." The cleaning and restoration processes are inefficient and no amount of energy output will keep the garment in its original state. Eventually the garment will reach a state of maximum entropy when it has degenerated into dust (a state of high disorder).

The same reasoning applies to the human body. Death causes the body to return to dust, or in other words, the body has now reached equilibrium with its surroundings. Death is a manifestation of the second law of thermodynamics.

The Second Law and Evolution

The second law of thermodynamics is an empirical law, directly observable in nature and in experimentation. This law implies that the direction of all natural processes is toward states of disorder. From the standpoint of statistics, natural operations proceed in a direction of greatest probability.[25] The most probable state for any natural system is one of disorder. All natural systems degenerate when left to themselves.

What about evolution and the second law? Huxley states that evolution is an irreversible process which leads to greater variety, to more complex, higher degrees of organization. His assertion contradicts the prediction of the direction of natural processes called for by the second law! Either evolution has occurred in spite of the second law, or evolution has not occurred at all.

There can be no question about the correctness and universality of the second law. How could evolution occur in spite of it? Many scientists would claim that most experiments conducted to verify this law are performed in closed systems. Biological systems are open systems (a system whose boundary is crossed by matter,[26] such as food intake and waste output).

Refuge Sought in Open Systems

Therefore, it is claimed that it is possible for evolution to occur in these open systems, since they may be immune to the effects of the second law. Such reasoning is not very convincing.

Most scientific theory and law has been developed in the way Kestin states:

In fact, in any branch of physics, the analysis of a phenomenon or process in terms of the relevant physical laws must begin by mentally isolating a collection of bodies from the rest.[27]

Normally, laboratory experiments are closed systems. The results obtained from such experiments usually are accepted by scientists without so much "fuss" about closed systems.

It would be possible to consider our solar system a closed system and observe the effects in this closed system. An analysis designed to obtain quantitative data is scientifically impossible; however, from general observations there is much qualitative data available. There is certainly a trend toward death, decay, and disorder, and no observable trend toward evolutionary development. There is obviously change and adaptation, but no evolution as called for by Huxley.

Open biological systems are subject to the second law. The entropy content of open systems may not increase as rapidly as that of closed

19

systems, but it does increase as evidenced by decay and death.

What about local decreases in entropy even though the entropy of the universe increases? Supposing millions and billions of years of local decreases in entropy, there would be countless exceptions to the second law in evolutionary development. Thus, some evolutionists reason that the second law would be overthrown so many times that it could not be considered law. Therefore, evolutionary development does not call for an occasional violation of the second law but for continual violations.

From the above pattern of ideas, one might deduce that the second law is really not scientific law; however, such a statement is preposterous! None of these violations is observed today, and it can only be postulated that they occurred in the past. The burden of proof rests on the man who makes such claims, and no satisfactory evidence can be given to support such an hypothesis. On the other hand the Christian can say that evolution has not occurred, because such a process is not scientific.

Another Argument: System Coupling

Another argument often presented and similar to the open system objection is that a system can be coupled to another. One system decreases

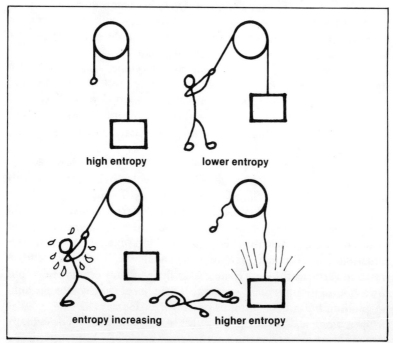

Figure 4 Coupling is not effective to permanently lower entropy of a system

in entropy while the system coupled to it increases greatly in entropy and the total for both systems is an entropy increase. Thus one system has decreased in entropy, but the second law has been obeyed.

An example of such a coupling may be observed when a person pulls a metal weight into the air by means of a pulley. The metal weight cannot spontaneously lift itself, but a person might lift it with a pulley, decreasing the entropy of the block. The energy waste in such an operation would cause a total entropy increase. To maintain the weight at this low entropy position, the person must continually pull the rope.

Eventually the person will get tired. Even if he is fed, he will finally weaken so that he must release the rope. (See Figure 4) the weight returns to the high entropy position. A constant restraint such as the one illustrated could cause a local entropy decrease. However, the coupling or restraint must be continually maintained. If the systems left alone or the force on it relaxed, the system will return to its most probable state.

Are there any such couplings or restraints now operating to "aid" the process of evolution? If they operated in the past, they must be operating now to hold the systems in a lower entropy state. Evolution requires natural causation and random changes. Such couplings or restraints must be beyond random processes because they must operate continually, and the process becomes controlled.

The couplings and restraints observed on biological systems do not cause any evolutionary development as stated by Huxley. No satisfactory evidence can be presented to show that such forces have produced any type of evolutionary process counter to the second law of thermodynamics. Again the burden of proof rests on those who claim it could have. To prove such a statement is an entirely different matter. Even as an organism grows, it is wearing out and will eventually die.

Conclusions

It seems more reasonable to believe that the existing order and complexity in the physical universe was created into it by God. Present scientific processes simply maintain that order and complexity. No new variety or more complex structure is coming into being. Only existing organisms are being modified. This view is consistent with the first law of thermodynamics.

The universal trend toward disorder and decay possibly was invoked when God cursed the creation because of Adam's sin.[28] The present complexity and order of the universe is decreasing. The rate of this degeneration is not a problem for thermodynamics. Rate processes are the concern of the field of kinetics. In the relatively new science of nonequilibrium thermodynamics, the rate of entropy production is a variable, but entropy always increases at a perceivable rate.[29, 30]

Scientific laws overrule the process of evolution. The two laws discussed in this paper call for conservative and degenerative processes operating together. Evolution is neither a conservative nor a degenerative process. Therefore it is concluded that evolution could not have occurred, since the first and second laws of thermodynamics would prevent any process that consistently produces greater order and complexity in the physical universe.

REFERENCES

[1]Crawford, Franzo H. 1963. Heat, thermodynamics and statistical physics. Harcort, Brace, and World, Inc., N.Y., p. 1

[2]Kestin, Joseph. 1966. A course in thermodynamics. Blaisdell, Waltham, Mass., p. 149.

[3]King, Allen L. 1962. Thermophysics. W. H. Freeman & Co., San Francisco, p. 5.

[4]Sears, Frances W. 1952. An introduction to thermodynamics, the kinetic theory of gases, and statistical mechanics, second edition. Addison-Wesley, Reading, p. 1.

[5]Crawford, *Op cit.*, p. 2.

[6]Darken, Lawrence S. and Robert W. Gurry. 1953. Physical chemistry of metals, McGaw-Hill, N.Y., p. 140.

[7]Huxley, Julian. 1955. Evolution and genetics, Chapter Eight (in) What is science? edited by J. R. Newman, Simon and Schuster, N.Y., p. 278.

[8]Fox, Sidney W. 1971. *Chemical and Enginering News,* 49 (50):46

[9]Crawford, *Op cit.*, p. 3.

[10]Fong, Peter. 1963. Foundations of thermodynamics. Oxford University Press, N.Y., p. 7.

[11]King, *op. cit.*, p. 7.

[12]*Loc cit.*

[13]Morris, Henry M. 1956. The bible and modern science. Moody Press. Chicago, p. 17.

[14]Kestin, *Op cit.*, p. 410.

[15]Fong, *Op. cit.*, p. 17.

[16]King, *Op. cit.*, p. 78.

[17]Fong., *Op. cit.*, p. 17.

[18]Crawford, *Op cit.*, p. 228.

[19]Kestin, *Op. cit.*, p. 411.

[20]Fong, *Op. cit.*, p. 17.

[21]King,*Op. cit.*, p. 103.

[22]Williams, Emmett L. 1970. Entropy and the solid state in Why not creation? edited by W. E. Lammerts. Creation Research Society Books, 5093 Williamsport Drive, Norcross, GA 30071, pp. 67-79.

[23]Hatsopoulous, George N. and Joseph H. Keenan. Principles of general thermodynamics. John Wiley & Sons., N.Y., p. 157.

[24]Crawford, *Op. cit.*, p. 258.

[25]Williams, *Op. cit.*

[26]Kestin, *Op. cit.*, p. 23.

[27]Kestin, *Op. cit.*, p. 22.

[28]Morris, Henry M. 1963. The twilight of evolution. Baker Book House, Grand Rapids.

[29]Hatsopoulous and Keenan, *Op. cit.*, p. 623.

[30]Fitts, Donald D. 1962. Nonequilibrium thermodynamics. McGraw-Hill, N.Y., p. 3.

II. Development And Stability Of Order

1

Order: Arrangement And Uniformity
Harold L. Armstrong

Introduction

Creationists often argue that the present great amount of order in the world could never have arisen spontaneously, as an evolutionist would have to maintain that it did. For what is observed is rather the opposite: if things are left to themselves, order decays and gives way to disorder. But it is commonly held, in the evolutionary worldview, that things began with disorder: a featureless cloud of stuff. The Creationist, then, can go on to point out that the train of events alleged under evolution could never, in fact, have happened.

The Creationists' point is well taken, and the argument valid. But some care is needed in stating what it meant by order. If "order" and "disorder" are not carefully defined, the argument may lose some of its force.

What is Meant by Order?

The first thing to be noted is that, in the present context, order does not necessarily mean uniformity. It is rather, to invent a word, *arrangedness*. It is conformity to some plan. In something which has parts, it is adaption of the parts to the whole, and of the whole to some plan.[1]

As a simple example, consider Figure 1. It illustrates a narrow trough, partly filled with water. Suppose that it were divided into ten divisions along its length, and the height also into discrete divisions, as shown. The divisions are considered discrete, and relatively few, for simplicity; there could, of course, be an infinite series of infinitesimal divisions.

If left to itself, the water would, as expected, come to the same level all along the trough, as shown for instance in part (a). Such a state of affairs would be one of equilibrium. The level of the water would be uniform, but it would not be particularly ordered.

Suppose, on the other hand, that the water should be somehow in the configuration shown in part (b). It is apparent, by adding the levels in the various parts, that the total amount of water is the same as in (a). But now the levels are arranged; they are ordered. So, from the present viewpoint, (b) shows order, (a) none.

23

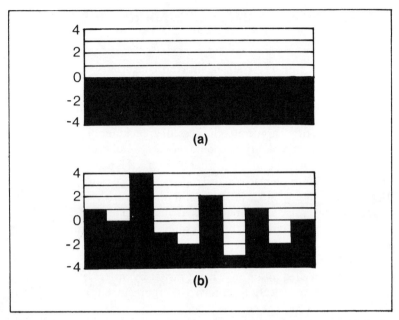

Figure 1. Part (a) shows the water in the water trough, used as an example in the text, in a state of equilibrium. Part (b) shows a situation which is not one of equilibrium, but to which rather there is some order, in the sense in which the term has been used here.

Toward a Definition of Order

What has just been given is an example; some kind of definition might be useful. A clue may be found by considering some definitions of energy, a very common notion in physics.

It is often said that the energy of a system, object, etc., is a measure of its ability to do mechanical work. In such a context, mechanical work will have been defined already, in the usual way as the product of a force and the distance through which something moves while the force is applied.

Such a definition, common though it is, may be objected to on at least three counts. First of all, the word "ability" may be thought to introduce a sort of anthropomorphic sound, which may not be wanted. In the second place, it would seem better that the definition involve what has already happened, not what may happen in the future. Finally, it may not, in fact, be possible to get mechanical work corresponding to all the energy, because of limitations which are considered along with the second law of thermodynamics.

24

It has been suggested that it is better to say that the energy of a system, object, etc., in a certain position, state, configuration, etc., is a measure of the mechanical work which was done, or might have been done, to get it into that position, etc.[2] "Might have been done" is added to allow for such cases as if, for instance, a watch should be built already wound.

Incidentally, a definition which says "a measure of" is a rather qualitative thing. It is common, in physics, to say that the energy is equal to the work. Then the definition becomes quantitative.

There is a difference, for "a measure of" need not mean "equal to", nor even "proportional to". Everybody would agree that temperature, in a qualitative way, is a measure of how hot a thing is. But for a quantitative description, temperature was at first taken as related linearly to the length of a column of mercury, or of some other suitable liquid. Nowadays, it would be taken as proportional to the pressure of a sample of a gas, under specified conditions. As a practical matter, those two quantitative definitions agree quite closely.

But a quite different definition would have been possible. For instance, the temperature might have been defined as proportional to the vapor pressure of a particular liquid under specified conditions. Such a definition could have been workable, and it would be quantitative. But it would not have coincided with the definitions mentioned previously. The relation between them would have been logrithmic and inverse.

In a sense, such different definitions are analogous to different scales. Commonly a scale is uniform, as on a ruler; and one in centimeters is proportional to one in inches. But a non-uniform scale, as for instance on logarithmic graph paper, is legitimate and may be useful.

Consider again Figure 1. Part (a) shows the system in equilibrium; in part (b) it has been arranged, or rearranged. So it might be said that the order of a system, from the present viewpoint, is a measure of the amount of rearrangement which was done, or might have been done, to take it from equilibrium to the condition in which it is. It appears that there will always be some sort of equilibrium for the systems considered in the present discussion, so there will always be some starting point from which to consider rearranging them.

The point has been made that order, in the sense in which the word is being used here, does not necessarily correspond to uniformity. For instance, the molecules of a gas, in equilibrium, are moving randomly, in all directions at all speeds. This is illustrated in Figure 2. The graph shows the numbers of molecules moving in the x-direction, say, at various speeds. As can be seen, some might be found with any speed; but there are more moving slowly than quickly.

25

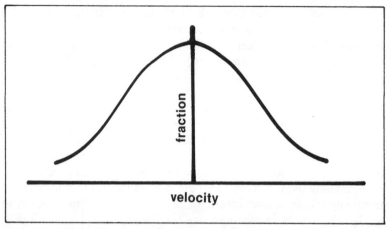

Figure 2. This shows, but not necessarily to scale, how the fraction of the molecules of a gas having one component of their velocity of a certain magnitude would vary with that magnitude.

On the other hand, all of the molecules in a sample might, in principle at least, be set moving in one direction at one speed. Something of the sort might happen if the gas could be squirted out of a nozzle at a very high speed. The situation would then be uniform, as far as the speeds are concerned, and it would be highly ordered. But it would be far from equilibrium.

Entropy and Order

Creationists often go on to associate lack of order, or disorder, with the entropy function, which has been defined in thermodynamics and in statistical mechanics. It is well known that in any spontaneous process the entropy increases, and correspondingly the order decreases. Again, the argument is valid; but again it is desirable to understand carefully just what is meant by order.

In fact, the order which is meant is the order of the kind which has just been discussed. Thus it may be worth while to look more closely at the connection between order and entropy.

Consider a system which may be divided into several parts, such that each of the parts might be in any of various possible states. For instance, the water trough, shown in Figure 1, is divided horizontally into ten parts; and the state of each part might be considered to the level of water in each part. (It is just for the sake of simplicity that only certain discrete levels are being considered at present.)

As for the gas, the parts could be the molecules; and the state of each could be its state of motion, maybe expressed in terms of the usual three coordinates.

The entropy S of the gas is already defined in statistical mechanics,[3] by:

$$S = -k \sum_i f_i \log f_i \qquad (1)$$

The states are considered as numbered, i being a representative number of a state. The number would relate to the speed; for instance, $i = 1,000$ might represent the state of moving in a certain direction, say the x-direction, at 1,000 centimetres per second. Thus there will be negative i's, as well as positive.

f_i is the fraction of the parts, i.e. of the molecules, which are in the state i, that is to say, moving at a certain speed. The summation will add the terms $f_i \log f_i$ for all the i's, that is for all speeds.

The logarithms are commonly taken to the base $e = 2.718. \ldots$; and then the constant k is Boltzmann's constant. Logarithms to some other base could be used by changing the constant. Since the f's, being fractions, are between zero and one, the logarithms will be negative; and thus the entropy will come out positive.

It is shown, in statistical mechanics, that the entropy, thus defined, coincides with that deduced by macroscopic considerations in thermodynamics. It is shown also that when the entropy is the maximum possible, subject to certain constraints, e.g. that the energy of the system remain fixed, the distribution of the velocities of the molecules is of the sort indicated in Figure 2. Maximum entropy, then, goes along with equilibrium; the entropy increases in the spontaneous processes by which the system approaches equilibrium. (Which any system will do, if allowed.)

It should be mentioned that in some problems, it is more satisfactory to deal, not with the entropy directly, but rather with the Gibbs or Helmholtz functions, which involve the entropy. But such a refinement does not seem to be needed here.

As was pointed out, the entropy of the gas, as defined, will be some positive magnitude, when the gas is in equilibrium. But suppose that it were in some ordered state. Suppose, for simplicity, that all of the molecules were moving in one direction at 1,000 centimeters per second. Then all of the parts — the molecules — would be in the state $i = 1,000$. So $f_{1,000}$ would be one, and all the rest of the f's zero. Now f log f is zero if f is zero or one. So all of the terms of the sum in Equation 1 would be zero, and thus the entropy zero. This shows how the entropy would be small in an ordered state, and larger in a state of equilibrium, which, from the present viewpoint, is disordered.

Now, how can such considerations be applied to the water trough, which was the example first taken? Well, there are ten parts: the ten horizontal divisions; and the state of each part can be the level of the water in it. There is, then, one part having level -3, two having + 1, etc. Since there are ten parts, the fraction f_{-3} would be 0.1, likewise f_{+1} would be 0.2, etc. All of the f's, for the arrangement shown, are listed in Table 1. Then the logarithms are taken, here to base 10 for simplicity, and the terms formed and added.

At this point the definition needs a little thought. The definition of entropy for the water trough need not be exactly the same as that for the molecules of a gas, which after all are something much different. Differences in definition come in even in energy. For instance, the potential energy of a heavy object, raised above the ground, would be proportional to its height. But that of a floating object, pushed under the water, would be proportional to its depth.

It is desired that the entropy for the water trough be a maximum at equilibrium, when the level is the same everywhere. At equilibrium, in fact, $f_0 = 1$, and all the other f's are zero. So, as already noted, the terms $f_i \log f_i$ would all be zero; and so would their sum. For the situation shown in (b), on the other hand, several of the f's are different from zero, but none as great as one. So there will be several negative terms $f \log f_i$.

But the situation shown in (b) is ordered; its entropy ought to be less than that at equilibrium. So define the entropy in this case, for the water trough:

$$S = \Sigma f_i \log f_i \qquad (2)$$

Thus the entropy will be zero for equilibrium, and negative for any ordered state; it will be a maximum at equilibrium, as desired. A constant term could have been added to the sum; but there seems to no advantage here in so doing. Incidentally, the question of an added constant arises also in macroscopic thermodynamics. There it may be arbitrary, or may be fixed by some rather involved considerations.

There seems no point in having, in Equation 2, a constant, different from one, corresponding to the k in Equation 1. For there is no question of making the result here agree with something from macroscopic thermodynamics.

As has already been noted, the condition of equilibrium would be the condition of minimum or no order, according to the present viewpoint. For one does not have to arrange equilibrium; it comes about spontaneously. But it is necessary to arrange a non-equilibrium situation;

and the arranging can be viewed as introducing order. Also, equilibrium is, with the limitations mentioned, a condition of maximum entropy.

Order was earlier called a measure of the rearrangement . . . Such a statement is qualitative. Now a quantitative statement will be offered.

It is suggested, then, that the order of a system, etc., in the sense which is being used here, be defined as the difference between the entropy of the system at equilibrium and that which applies for the situation in question. Since the entropy is a maximum at equilibrium, that difference will be positive for any other state, corresponding to some order — some rearrangement. If the system in question should be one for which entropy is already defined through thermodynamics or statistical mechanics, that entropy may as well be used. If not, an entropy may be invented for the purpose, as it has been for the water trough. However, it may be desirable, in some cases, to add a constant to the entropy according to some previous definition, so as to have the amount of order zero at equilibrium. This should cause no trouble, for the entropy as commonly defined may already contain an added constant.

For instant, as is shown in Table 1, the entropy, according to the proposed definition, of the water trough in the situation (b) comes to be of magnitude -0.82, to two places of decimals, whereas in the equilibrium situation, (a), it would be zero. Thus the numerical magnitude assigned to the order shown in (b), according to the present proposal, would be 0.82.

i	f_i	$\log f_i$	$f_i \log f_i$
-3	0.1	-1.0	-0.10
-2	0.2	-0.7	-0.14
-1	0.1	-1.0	-0.10
0	0.2	-0.7	-0.14
+1	0.2	-0.7	-0.14
+2	0.1	-1.0	-0.10
+3	0.0	-	0.00
+4	0.1	-1.0	-0.10
			-0.82

Table 1. This shows the f's corresponding to the various states i as shown in Figure 1 (b), and the further calculations from them to arrive at the entropy, and the numerical order, to be assigned to the situation.

The Jet of Air

As was pointed out earlier, according to the definition from statistical mechanics, if all of the molecules of a gas, say ordinary air, were moving in the same direction at the same speed, and, for instance, it had just been squirted out in an extremely high-speed jet, the entropy would be zero. Later, however, after the air had settled down to equilibrium, the entropy would be greater, having some finite magnitude.

An attempt will be made here to do some calculation about this matter. However, there are complications. For while the air is still in a jet, it is by no means in a state of equilibrium; so neither the determination of entropy by macroscopic thermodynamics nor even that by the usual kind of statistical mechanics applies. On the other hand, when the gas will have settled down to equilibrium, the entropy may be determined in either of those ways; but it introduces things which are irrelevant for the present purposes. In view of these considerations, a sort of quasi-, or maybe pseudo-, entropy will be used.

For the jet, then, while it is still a jet, the entropy will be set at zero, as already suggested.

It is shown in statistical mechanics that a gas, in equilibrum has the fraction of the molecules having speeds of u, v, and w, in the x, y, and z directions respectively, proportional to:[4]

$$\left(\frac{m}{2 \pi kT} \right)^{3/2} e^{- \frac{m(u^2 + v^2 + w^2)}{2 kT}} \tag{3}$$

So use that as the fraction f, and carry out the procedure suggested in and around Equation 1. There will be this difference, though: here there is an infinite lot of infinitesimal divisions; so the summation becomes an integral. In fact, it becomes:

$$S = k \left(\frac{m}{2kT} \right)^{3/2} \int_{-\infty}^{\infty} \int_{-\infty}^{\infty} \int_{-\infty}^{\infty} \left\{ \frac{m(u^2 + v^2 + w^2)}{2kT} \right.$$

$$\left. + \frac{3}{2} \log \left(\frac{2\pi kT}{m} \right) \right\} e^{- \frac{m(u^2 + v^2 + w^2)}{2kT}} \, du \, dv \, dw \tag{4}$$

The integration can be carried out, as shown in Reference 4. When that is done, and some algebraic simplification applied, the result is:

$$S = \frac{3k}{2} \left\{ \frac{2\pi kT}{m} \right\}^{3/2} \left\{ \log \left(\frac{2\pi kT}{m} \right) + 1 \right\} \tag{5}$$

Now for some evaluation. Suppose that the temperature is 300 on the absolute scale, which is approximately 27 °C, a somewhat warm room temperature. m is the mass of the molecule concerned. There is, of course, no such thing as a molecule of air. Yet air may be treated as a gas of molecular weight approximately 29; and the mass of a molecule of such a (hypothetical) gas would be 29 x 1.66 x 10^{-24} = 5.47 x 10^{-23} gm. Also, in the units used here k = 1.38 x 10^{-16}.

So when all of this is put together, the (quasi- or pseudo-) entropy at equilibrium comes to be of magnitude 1.58. Since it was represented as zero for the jet, the numerical order of the situation represented by the jet of air is of magnitude 1.58. (arbitrary units.) The logarithm was taken to base e.

There are anomalies in this calculation. For instance, the differentials du, dv, and dw should have been counted in somehow in the logarithm. In statistical mechanics as ordinarily presented, similar considerations lead to a constant term in the entropy, which may be either left undetermined or may be fixed by rather involved considerations which seem quite foreign to the present purpose.

The other anomaly is this: nothing has been said directly about the amount of air involved. Perhaps, however, such a thing was not really needed. All that was desired here was to get an entropy-like expression whence the numerical order could be calculated, as was proposed. That has been done. In particular, it may be noted that here, and contrary to what was found in the previous example, order, in the sense in which the term is used here, and uniformity do go together. These two contrasted cases, then, illustrate the fact that there is no necessary connection between uniformity and order in the sense being used here. Each case must be considered in the light of its own peculiarities.

The Equalization of Temperatures

Two cases have been discussed so far. In the one, the entropy-like function which was introduced had really not much to do with entropy in the usual thermodynamic sense. In the other, the gas jet, the connection was closer, but there was still something quasi - or pseudo- about the entropy used.

Now a case will be considered in which the entropy in the ordinary thermodynamic sense will serve for the discussion of order.

Consider two blocks of copper, for which the specific heat, taken as constant over the range of temperature concerned, is about 0.093 calories per gram per degree, each block weighing one kilogram. Suppose that they were each very well insulated, except on one face; and that having been brought to different temperatures, they were put with the lightly insulated faces together. They would, of course, come to the same temperature.[5]

When they are at the same temperature they will be at equilibrium, as far as their relation one to the other is concerned. But the system of the two blocks will be more ordered, in the present sense of the term, when they are at different temperatures.

Suppose, for a certain neatness (although it is not absolutely necessary) that the one block is heated, the other cooled, and by equal amounts. Thus their average temperature will remain at the temperature of the surroundings, which will be taken as 23 °C. So when the blocks will have come to equilibrium with each other, they will be also in equilibrium with the surroundings.

If it seems helpful, one may think of a rather light thermal insulation between the blocks where they are together. That could slow down the flow of heat from the hotter to the cooler, so that the metal itself of each block would always be at (approximately) the same temperature.

Let the one block, then, be heated by θ °C, to 23 + θ °C, the other cooled by θ °C to 23 − θ °C; then let them be put together. It will suffice to consider the change in entropy as they come to equilibrium.

As the warmer block changes in temperature by an amount -dT, its temperature being T, its entropy will decrease by an amount mc dT/T. Here m is the mass, c the specific heat. In the same time, the cooler one will take in the same amount of heat. So its entropy will increase by a similar term. However, its temperature will be different; so in the expression for its change of entropy (which will be an increase) there will be a different T in the denominator. The T's in the denominators are expressed in the absolute scale. Recall also that 23 + θ °C = 296 + θ on the absolute scale; likewise 23 − θ °C = 296 − θ.

The change in entropy, then, in coming to equilibrium is:

$$93 \int_{296-\theta}^{296} \frac{dT}{T} - 93 \int_{296}^{296+\theta} \frac{dT}{T} = 93 \log_e \left(\frac{296}{296-\theta} \frac{296}{296+\theta} \right) \quad (6)$$

The numerical order, then, representing the fact that the system of two blocks or ordered, i.e. arranged, when they are at different temperatures, is, for an initial difference in temperature 2θ , equal in magnitude to the change of entropy just found.

Figure 3 shows how the order, in the present sense, increases with increasing difference in the temperatures of the two blocks. If they are at the same temperature, there is no order; as the difference increases, so does the amount of order, in the present sense. Thus this is another case in which uniformity and order do not coincide.

Another Name

Brillouin, in particular, has used the term "negentropy", which, as the name suggests, is just the negative of the entropy.[6] Thus the

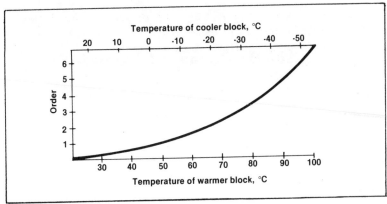

Figure 3. This shows the numerical order, as it has been defined, of the system of the two blocks of copper, the one having been heated above the equilibrium temperature of 23 °C, the other cooled an equal amount.

numerical order, proposed here, differs from the negentropy mostly in respect to constants, and especially in being adjusted to be zero at equilibrium.

Otherwise, the use of the word "order" can be defended in that it refers immediately to a notion which it intuitively important, and in that a simple name has been substituted for a "crackjaw" one.

On Considering the Appropriate Thing

In relating order to entropy, as proposed here, the definition of entropy appropriate to the problem being considered must, of course, be used. For instance, in discussing the water trough, the entropy used was related to the arrangement of the water.

But an entropy could be assigned to the water, in terms of ordinary macroscopic thermodynamics, having to do with the heat taken in, in a way similar to what was done for the copper, around Equation 6. Such an entropy, of course, would have nothing to do with the question of order or otherwise in the level of the water.

References

[1]Armstrong, H.L., 1978. Thermodynamics, energy, matter, and form. *Creation Reserach Society Quarterly* 15 (2): 119-121, and (3): 167-168 & 174.

[2]*Ibid.*

[3]Slater, J.C., 1939. Introduction to chemical physics. 1st edition, 6th impression. McGraw-Hill. Chapter III.

[4]*Ibid.*, Chapter IV, especially p. 56.

[5]Armstrong, H.L., 1975. Use of the second law of thermodynamics in macroscopic form in Creation studies. *Creation Research Society Quarterly* 12 (2): 103-106.

[6]Brillouin, Leon, 1956. Science and information theory. Academic Press, New York. P. 116, and many subsequent places.

2

The Development Of Order

David R. Boylan

Introduction

One of the most difficult concepts in the understanding of origins is the mechanism for the development of order. The problem has arrested the attention of much of the scientific community. Indeed, the "riddle" of life is this development. As is true of many scientific mysteries, explanations advanced for the "first cause" in the development of order in the universe or in living systems depend heavily upon the philosophy of the interpreter. Some have accepted the thesis that supernatural explanations can not be used to explain the origin of the universe or the complexity of life, and as a consequence, have proposed various mechanisms based on natural processes. Others have accepted the concept of the supernatural in the matter of origins and find a very fundamental relationship between the operation of the universe and a creationistic explanation. The issue, of course, will not be settled in a scientific forum, for origins are indeed outside of the true province of science, and data based on our present time span is far too short to make generalizations valid. It is the purpose of this paper to examine some of the hypotheses for the development of order by a consideration of the processes which are believed to have been involved.

Order in System

Few serious scientists doubt that there has been a development of order from simple forms to the present extremely complex living systems. Regardless of cause, we observe order in the universe which allows us to predict projectories to distant planets, to measure the Einsteinian effect of gravity on light, to define the evasive concept of light quanta, to establish a clocking system and to confirm our concepts of gravity, motion, and energy. But far exceeding the order in the physical universe is the observable order in the living world and the complexity of living systems. An analysis of the human body alone shows remarkably complex systems. A few of these are well known—the eye system, the ear system, the circulatory system, the nervous system, the thought system, the reproductive system, the self-healing system, the editing system in DNA, and the sensory system. Many of these systems exist in less complicated form in living systems at the cellular level, but it is a strange fact that *all* living systems are extremely complex. Scientists do not yet clearly understand the basic metabolism of the simplest cell. The question, then, is how could such systems have developed?

Proposed Processes

One philosophy is that these systems developed by natural processes and that evolutionary changes occur by natural selection acting on the wide variation in the gene pool to produce a "survival of the fittest" population. This concept rests heavily upon random chance, operating through long-time spans. Not all scientists agree with this proposal.

There is the ever-present feeling amongst some that processes which will not go readily in our present world under laboratory conditions are not likely to go under conditions in which the process is not so easily controlled. Contrary to Dr. Wald's assertion that

> ". . . the important point is that since the origin of life belongs in the category of at-least-once phenomena, time is on our side. However improbably we regard this event. . . , given enough time it will almost certainly happen at least once. . . . Time is in fact the hero of the plot. . . . Given so much time, the impossible becomes possible, the possible probable, and the probable virtually certain, one has only to wait; time itself performs miracles."[1]

The operation of improbable events over long time spans as a mechanism of the development of order is considered by many to be "grasping for a straw."

One of the most vexing problems in a naturalistic explanation of order is to account for the decrease in entropy required for the development of ordered systems. Dr. Weisskopf has proposed that the general cooling of the universe is responsible for this decrease in entropy.

> "It is the temperature gradient between the hot sun and the colder earth that produced the living order, ever changing and developing through reproduction and evolution."[2]

Dr. Prigogine has proposed that "dissipative structures" under non-equilibrium conditions can be a source of negative entropy.

> ". . . A new order principle appears that corresponds es-

sentially to an amplification of fluctuations and to their ultimate stabilization by the flow of matter and energy from the surroundings. We may call this principle 'order through fluctuations.' "[3]

Dr. Brillouin has suggested that some "life force" is yet to be discovered.

". . . Consider a living organism; it has special properties which enable it to resist destruction, to heal its wounds, and to cure occasional sickness. This is very strange behavior, and nothing similar can be observed about inert matter. Is such behavior an exception to the second principle? It appears so, at least superficially, and we must be prepared to accept a "life principle" that would allow for some exceptions to the second principle."[4]

Many have suggested that the answer lies in the "open system" concept.

Open Systems

The last explanation seems to be the most common. That is, that living systems are "open" systems and therefore receive the necessary energy from outside the living system itself. This view suggests that the second law of thermodynamics is fully satisfied for the development of complexity in the living system at the expense of some energy source from the surroundings. Such an explanation has merit, since our understanding of all processes is that they conform to the second principle, and unless living systems are entirely different from other systems, and therefore not natural systems, the total entropy change of the system and surroundings must be positive. If living systems are systems of negative entropy change then energy must be supplied in at least as great a quantity with a positive entropy change in the surroundings. Such explanations, however, give little attention to the source or the particularity of the energy which might be available in the open system market. Overlooked is the "quality" of the energy required to provide the ordering necessary in the development of the complex living system. It stands to reason that just any form of energy from the sun could not qualify as a productive source for the development of order. Extended discussion of this was presented in an article[5] dealing with process constraints. In that article, the concept of "ordered" or "non-random" energy was introduced as an appropriate term in the first law expression

36

around any process. The term W_o was shown to be equivalent to other energy sources which need to be included in the energy balance.* Other energy sources such as magnetic, electro-chemical, W_e, and surface tension, W_c, are also necessary for some processes. Each of these energy sources is important in specific applications, but usually ignored in ordinary processes. None of the first law terms generally used, including those just mentioned, have been shown to be order producing, and therefore, in a system in which order is enhanced, some unique energy source must be envisioned. Examination of the conventional terms in the first law expression is futile in an attempt to find a source which produce order from disorder or complexity from simplicity.

Ordered Systems

A first law expression can be written around the random mixing of red and black balls in a box under isothermal conditions, where no work is extracted, no heat added, and no other outside energy forces of significance in operation shows the final state to be totally random. If, however, an ordering of the red and black balls occurs (either as all red in one end and all black in the other, or as a very definite pattern of red and black) an energy source is evident which "sorts" on the basis of color. That source is the energy of ordering, W_o. The question of course remains as to where the energy ordering arises. In the creationst view, W_o is the creative work involved. In the naturalistic viewpoint, W_o is resident in the natural forces at work in the universe. It remains, therefore, to be seen just what natural forces can produce order.

Although criticism is made that the creationist takes an easy way out by assigning this W_o to a Creator, it is nevertheless a rational conclusion based on evidence. It does not call for imagined effects of long time spans and the hoped for potential of natural selection.

Dr. Schrodinger, along with others, earlier proposed that the energy source for the development of system complexity is a result of the flow of negative entropy from the surroundings.

"... A living organism continually ... produces positive entropy ... and thus tends to approach the dangerous state of maximum entropy, which is death. It can only keep ... alive by continually drawing from its environment negative entropy. . ."[6]

*See appendix for a summary of the discussion from reference 5.

Cooling Systems

This "negative entropy" is postulated to come from cooling of the surroundings. Crystallization is often used as an example of natural ordering. The argument is that since the crystal is an ordered state known to occur by natural evaporation in large lakes, the process of cooling produces order.

There are two major objections to this viewpoint. One is that cooling does not produce crystallization, if by cooling is meant a lowering of temperature. Most students in physical chemistry are aware of this. A common laboratory experiment is to plot a cooling curve to get the "ice" point. The resulting plot is graphic evidence that crystallization is not a result of cooling. It *is* a result of the molecular forces operating at a particular temperature. Cooling is simply a preparation for crystallization.

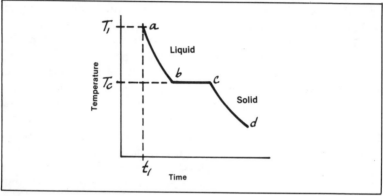

Figure 1 Typical cooling curve

Figure 1 is a typical cooling curve for a liquid. If the liquid is initially at point a on the graph, represented by a certain temperature T_1 and time t_1, upon cooling (i.e. lowering of its temperature) the change of temperature with time, assuming a constant withdrawal of heat from the liquid, is shown by the line a to b. During this process, the temperature of the original liquid is lowered. However, the molecules are in random motion and no crystallization takes place. At point b, the freezing point, T_c, (barring super-saturation and super-cooling effects) crystallization is initiated. Crystallization occurs *at a constant temperature represented by* T_c, *and occurs completely without change in temperature.* In fact, the temperature can not be lowered beyond temperature T_c until crystallization is complete. When crystallization is complete at point c, cooling takes place again by a change from point c to point d, but no crystallization takes place in this cooling process. So, crystallization does not qualify as an energy source for financing life processes. In fact, the crystallization process is actually a result of resident forces in the liquid which are effective at a particular, definite temperature, T_c. This phenomenon must be explained in terms other than random chance and natural selection.

The second problem with the concept that cooling can produce a flow of negative entropy and therefore provide the energy for ordering needed in the development of the complexity of life, is that it is self-terminating. Even if it be accepted that crystallization is an ordered product of random cooling, what can a crystal do to order the next step in the development of further order toward the complexity of life? Even though random chance might produce a crystal, the crystal itself can not produce a higher order than is specified by its atomic structure. Therefore, it is impossible to call upon the processes of crystallization to finance the development of order.

Dissipative Structures

This same argument must be used with Prigogine's thesis that dissipative structures have a particular order and, as a result, can finance the negative entropy change necessary for the development of life. Even a steady state solution to the conservation of mass equation,

$$\partial x_i / \partial t = D_i \nabla^2 x_i + V_i(\{x_j\}) \tag{1}$$

with which Prigogine worked, is self-terminating. Such configuration or "order" is totally impotent to produce a higher level of ordering and, therefore, not able to contribute to a continued development of complexity.

Chemical Evolution

It is assumed in a scientific analysis of living systems that the processes involved are to be understood by ordinary chemistry and physics. Dr. Calvin states that

> "Life is a logical consequences of known chemical principles operating on the atomic composition of matter."[7]

Dr. Calvin proposes possible processes in terms of present-day chemistry.

> "In the beginning most of the elements of the universe were in the form of hydrogen, which eventually had to undergo fusion reactions, giving rise to higher elements in the periodic

table, particularly those important to living things: carbon, nitrogen, oxygen, sulfur, phosphorous, halides and certain metals, particularly iron, which are important catalytic functions in living organisms.

Then the primitive (prebiotic, primeval) molecules were formed from the organogenic elements with which the earth was initially coated: methane, ammonia, carbon monoxide, water, carbon dioxide, hydrogen sulfide, and of course, hydrogen. These first three stages present no chemical problem, since the first two are nuclear and the third is simply the result of presence of carbon, hydrogen, nitrogen and oxygen at a low enough temperature to produce the small primitive molecules.

The next stage of chemical evolution—from the organogenic molecules to the biomonomers—does present a chemical problem, and it has been an area of major progress in the last twenty years. . . The conversion of organogenic molecules into amino acids, sugars, nucleic acid bases, and other carboxylic acids (acetic acid and citric acid) has been achieved in the laboratory under the influence of a wide variety of energy sources, ranging from the ultraviolet light of the sun to to radioactive energy (in the form of ionizing radiation) to mechanical energy (in the form of meteoritic shock waves). All these energy sources give rise to the transformation of the organogenic molecule to biomonomers.

The next state—the transition from biomonomers to biopolymers—is more difficult to achieve in terms of chemical evolution . . .which eventually gave rise to the first living organisms about four million years ago."[8]

These processes are given in Figure 2 and summarized in Table I which shows the processes proposed by Calvin from the "origin" or hydrogen state to the complex systems, as chemical reactions. In this table, generalized formulas for the major steps in the development of order have been used. Some of these processes are well-known. Others are only conceived.

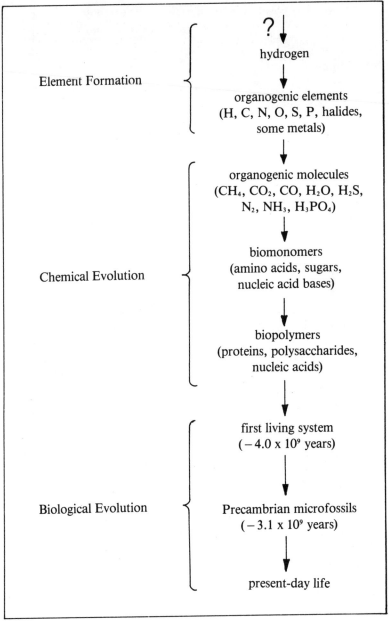

Figure 2 Time sequence of evolution from formation of elements to the present (from Calvin p. 171)

TABLE 1
TYPICAL REACTIONS FOR POSTULATED DEVELOPMENT OF COMPLEX LIVING SYSTEMS

TYPICAL REACTIONS	HEAT OF REACTION (ΔH)	ENTROPY CHANGE (ΔS)	EQUILIBRIUM CONSTANT (K)
1. Element Formation			
$_1H^1 + _{-1}e^0 + _0\eta^0 + Q_1 + 3.6\ MeV \rightarrow _0\eta^1$	$+\ \Delta H$ (High)	$-\ \Delta S^*$ (High)	Small
$H_2 + x\ _1H^1 + y\ _{-1}e^0 + 3_0\eta^0 + Q_2 \rightarrow$ various atomic species	$+\ \Delta H$ (High)	$-\ \Delta S^*$ (High)	Small
2. Organogenic Molecules			
a. $C + 2H_2 \rightarrow CH_4$	-17.9 K cal/mol	$-\ \Delta S$ (Med.)	Medium
b. $H_2 + O_2 \rightarrow 2H_2O$	-57.8 K cal/mol	$-\ \Delta S$ (Med.)	Medium
$N_2 + 3H_2 \rightarrow 2NH_3$	-11.04 K cal/mol	$-\ \Delta S$ (Med.)	Medium
d. etc.			
3. Biomonomers			
a.	> -100 K cal/mol	$-\ \Delta S$ (Med.)	Low

a.

$$\begin{array}{c} R \\ | \\ H-C=O \end{array} + H-C\equiv N + H-O-H \rightarrow$$

$$\begin{array}{c} H \\ \diagdown \\ N-C-C-O-H \\ H \diagup \quad | \quad \diagdown \\ \quad H \quad O \end{array} \quad (Amino\ Acids)$$

3. b. $H-C\equiv N \rightarrow H-C$ ⟶ Adenine	$-\ \Delta H$ (Med.)	$-\ \Delta S$ (Med.)	Low
4. Biopolymers			
a. Biomolomers → Pyrimidines + Purines	$-\ \Delta H$	$-\ \Delta S$ (Med.)	Very Low
b. Pyrimidines + Purines → Deoxyribonucleic Acids	$-\ \Delta H$	$-\ \Delta S$ (Med.)	Very Low
5. Living Systems			
a. Nucleic Acids → Proteins	$-\ \Delta H$	$-\ \Delta S$	Very Low
b. Proteins + Enzymes → Complex Forms	$-\ \Delta H$	$-\ \Delta S$	Very Low
c. Complex Forms → Living Systems	$-\ \Delta H$	$-\ \Delta S$ ** (Extremely High)	Extremely Low

*Actual ΔS is a result of nuclear reaction heat effects.

** Actual ΔS must include an information processing term, or ordering effect.

Many of the processes leading to the formation of DNA or protein molecules are extraordinarily complex. A chart of the Metabolic Pathways, published by the Calbiochem-Behring Co., is four feet by five feet in size, just to clearly show all of the reactions involved. Table I is, of course, a gross simplification, and is used only to illustrate the processes that must be considered. For each typical process the nature of the process is shown in terms of the $\triangle$ H, the enthalpy change; $\triangle$ S, the entropy change; and K, the equilibrium constant. It may be noted that most of the processes are quite common and experimentally reproducible, such as those involving initial compound formation, the development of pre-biotic compounds, the combination of pre-biotic compounds into amino acids and subsequent development of proteins, and the combination of proteins into organo-molecules and complex organic chemicals. However, the processes of element formation and of initiation of life are not common and have not been reproduced in the laboratory. Calvin's dismissal of the first as "... these ...stages present no chemical problem, since the first two are nuclear ..."[9] is unfortunate, as an understanding of element formation is the *essential* step in understanding subsequent chemical evolution or development. In this stage and in the initiation of life, the required entropy changes are unaccounted for in naturalistic terms. In fact, all of the processes after the initial development of the elements into the various compounds depend heavily upon the energy state of the chemical elements themselves. This state, as shown, is possible only by extremely high energy absorption. It is important also to note that the development of the elements assumes the pre-existence of hydrogen or its constitutents.

Driving Forces

The energy source for the development of the elements as shown in Table I must be supplied from something other than nature since there could have been no "natural" sources. The creationist finds it easy to describe this energy source as a creative act. In like manner, the development of complex molecules into living system requires an ordering energy not possible in the molecules themselves. There must have been some "outside" energy director.

Dr. Cloud states that
"The chemical elements themselves, the perception of whose ordered arrangements is one of the great artistic triumphs of science, are cooked in stars, novae, and supernovae as a product of the enormous temperatures found there. *Energy from the sun,* through photosynthesis, *is the driving force* of *life and its evolution* ...."[10]

43

What Dr. Cloud overlooks in this conclusion is that photosynthesis is the "energy director" and is *necessary* to the utilization of the sun's energy. Obviously, a *necessary* component of a system cannot be called upon to initiate the system itself! Photosynthesis relies upon a living system to provide energy direction. The development of order by photosynthesis using energy from the sun is circular reasoning because it assumes the desired result. To develop complexity in terms of living, functional systems of complex molecules requires the W_o term referred to earlier.[11] It requires a source of ordered energy NOT resident in the system itself.

What processes can be called upon to provide the negative entropy required for living systems development? The Creationist's viewpoint is that the negative entropy has been inserted into the instructions residing in the DNA Molecule that code it for development. This code has been shown by Quinn not to be random.

> "In the research reported, a case is made for existence of a highly-ordered genetic control system that expresses itself in messages written in the form of *intelligible* codons. These codons are intelligent in the sense of being able to recognize each other and anticipate how they will interact upon translation into corresponding polypeptide chains, in vivo. . . ."[12]

The equilibrium for any reaction or process is derivable from heat quantities alone. These heat quantities are related as follows:
The Gibbs free energy, G, is defined as

$$G = U + PV - TS \qquad (2)$$

where: U = internal energy   P = pressure   T = temperature
   S = entropy

and since, $H = U + PV$, and $G = H - TS$ $\qquad$ (3)

For a given reaction Equation 2 can be written $\triangle G = \triangle H - \triangle(TS)$ at constant temperature and standard states,

$$\triangle G^\circ = \triangle H^\circ - T\triangle S^\circ \qquad (4)$$

This free energy change is related to equilibrium by

$$\triangle G^\circ = - RT \ln K \qquad (5)$$

where K is the equilibrium constant.

By combining Equations 4 and 5 an expression for the equilibrium constant in terms of entropy and enthalphy is obtained as

$$-RT \ln K = \triangle H° - T\triangle S° \qquad (6)$$

which can be written

$$\ln K = \frac{-\triangle H°}{RT} + \frac{\triangle S°}{R} \qquad (7)$$

According to Stull, these

". . . relationships clearly indicate that the atoms present in a reaction will prefer the molecular configurations in which the entropy is maximized and in which the energy is minimized (algebraically). The maximum entropy is associated generally with the molecular configurations having the largest number of states available to the system, thus providing more "freedom" for the system. The minimum energy is associated generally with the molecular structure in which its atoms are most strongly bound to each other (or the structures in which the atoms will have the maximum stability)" . . . "At low temperatures the equilibrium is determined largely by the value of $\triangle H°$, the "stability" term, while at high temperatures the equilibrium is determined largely by the value of the $\triangle S°$, the 'freedom' term."[13]

In considering the typical reactions in Table I, it is to be noted that except for element formation and living systems development, most of the heats of reaction as well as the entropy changes are moderate. For these processes, the equilibrium constant is moderately positive. These reactions are common reactions or ones which can be reproduced by careful experimental technique. The nature of these reactions is generally such that the entropy of the product is less than the sum of the entropies of the component reactants. Thus, negative entropy changes have been shown. General experience is that the change in entropy accompanying a given reaction is related to the increase or decrease in the total number of states of existence available to the system in the form of products over the number of states of existence available in the form of reactants.

In general, the equilibrium constant will be large for reactions where the product molecules are the ones predominating at equilibrium and will be small where the reactants are predominating at equilibrium. However, the equilibrium constant shown by Equation 7 is dependent upon $\triangle H°$ and $\triangle S°$. It will be greatest for reactions where products have a maximum value of $\triangle S°$ and a minimum value $\triangle H°$. It is clear that atoms constituting the molecules involved will tend to go preferentially into those molecular configurations in which entropy is greatest and in which the heat content is lowest. The greatest entropy is in general associated with those molecular configurations having the largest number of states of existence. However, the lowest heat content is, in general, associated with those molecular configurations in which the atoms are bound most securely one to another.

The final state of equilibrium, as estimated in Table I, is determined by a compromise between the above two opposing tendencies. The equilibrium constant at high temperatures is determined largely by the value of $\triangle S°$. Whereas, the equilibrium constant at low temperatures is determined largely by the value of $\triangle H°$. The equilibrium constraints in Table I are estimated levels only, based on the probable reaction heats and entropy changes involved.

It should be pointed out that definitions derived from the second law of thermodynamics in regard to entropy changes do not specify the effects of these entropy changes. Some entropy changes are simply the result of heat removal or additions, since $\triangle S$ is usually calculated

$$\text{from} \quad \triangle S = \int \frac{dQ}{T} \tag{8}$$

it may be negative or positive depending upon the removal or addition of heat. The concept of entropy, however, goes beyond heat removal or addition, as has been shown in statistical and information theory; and $\triangle S$ represents the change in energy states of the system before and after an event. A system whose total energy is less available exhibits a positive entropy change. One whose energy availability is higher after the change exhibits a negative entropy change. In information theory, a positive entropy change indicates a loss in information during the transmission of information from one state to another. In like manner, the decrease in order in a process or as a result of a process represents a positive entropy change. Such systems can not be characterized simply by heat interchange with the surroundings, but by the ability of the system to do work or by the total availability of the energy of the system after the change. If ordering is considered in the atomic structure as opposed to the subatomic units, the entropy change cannot be calculated by heat input, but by a consideration of probability and statistical inference. For the latter case, a negative entropy change would be shown. In either case, the effect is large and significant. The energy input to the element formation is in reality the resource for all subsequent chemical reactions. This can be considered either as energy content or resident information in the atomic structure.

Richard E. Dickerson in an article dealing with chemical evolution and the origin of life says:

"We can divide the problem of evoluton of living cells from non-living matter into five steps: 1) the formation of the planet with gases in the atmosphere that could serve as raw materials for life; 2) the synthesis of biological monomers, such as amino acids, sugars and organic bases; 3) the polymerization of such monomers into primitive protein and nucleic acid chains in an aqueous environment where depolymerization is thermodynamically favored; 4) the segregation of droplets of Haldane soup into protobionts with a chemistry and an identity of their own and 5) the development of some type of reproductive machinery to ensure that the daughter cells have all the chemical and metabolic capabilities of the parent cells. Stated concisely, these are the problems of raw materials monomers, polymers, isolation and reproduction."[14]

The problem associated with demonstrating this concept is not solved, as Dickerson states:

"It is one thing to propose scenarios for the origin of life that might have been; it is another thing entirely to demonstrate that such scenarios are either possible or probable. As evidence, there is a meager record of fossil microorganisms, a geological history of the planet, laboratory experiments that can demonstrate what primitive reactions *might* have been possible, extra-terrestrial evidence for organic matter in meteorites, and in spectra of interstellar dust and the *hope* of detecting life that evolved independently on other planets."[15] (emphasis added)

Dickerson continues

"Two cautionary comments are necessary. Although the simulations (of Miller and Urey) yield many of the amino acids found in the proteins of living organisms, they also yield at least as many related molecules that are not present. For example, experiments of the Miller type synthesize three isomeric forms of an amino acid with the formula $C_3H_7NO_2$:

47

alanine, β-alanine and sarcosine. Yet only alanine has been incorporated into the proteins of living organisms. Of the three isomers, valine, isovaline and norvaline, only valine appears in proteins today. Seven amino acid isomers with the formula $C_4H_9NO_2$ are created in spark discharge experiments, none of which is designated as a protein constituent by the universal genetic code of terrestrial life. It is obvious that the choice of the 20 amino acids in the genetic code was not foreordained by the availability of a particular set of molecules on the primitive earth. One of the fascinating side issues of origin of life biochemistry is why the present set of 20 amino acids was chosen."[16]

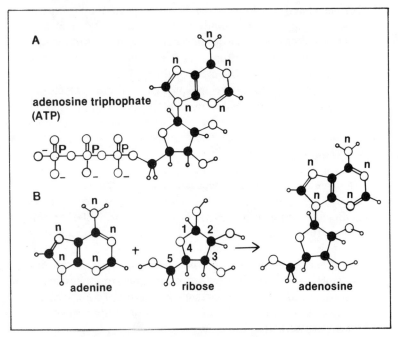

Figure 3 Adenosine triphosphate (ATP), the principal medium for the storage and exchange of energy in all living organisms, is created from adenine, ribose, and a triphosphate tail (A). The non-biological synthesis of adenosine presents a special difficulty because the adenine might be coupled to anyone of the four carbons in the ribose (1 ', 2 ', 3 ', or 5 ') that carries a hydroxyl group (B). Moreover, three of the four hydroxyl carbons (1 ', 2 ', and 3 ') are asymmetric so that alpha and beta forms of the molecule can be synthesized at each of them. In organisms today adenine and ribose are coupled at the 1 ' carbon in the beta configuration of the molecule.

48

"The other cautionary observation is that the laboratory simulations of pre-biological reactions give rise to equal numbers of both forms of optically active molecules: molecules that rotate polarized light in opposite directions because the molecules exist in two configurations that are a mirror image of each other. Such molecules are designated by the prefix D or L, abbreviations for dextro and levo, designating the direction of rotation of the polarized light. Except for certain special adaptations involving bacterial cell walls and biochemical defense mechanisms, all living organisms today incorporate only L amino acids. . . It seems likely that the primitive selection of the L isomers over the D isomers was a matter of chance. . ."[17]

"It is not difficult to account for the appearance of the bases and sugars of nucleic acids on the primitive earth. An unexpected stumbling block arises, however, when one tries to account for the particular way in which the bases and sugars are joined to make nucleotides, such as the coupling of adenine and ribose to form adenosine molecules."

"No one has yet proposed a convincing method of getting good yields of the beta-1 ′ connection between adenine and ribose that is universally found in DNA and RNA."[18]

Further, in discussing whether experiments have produced life, Dickerson states:

"This is not life, but it is getting close to it. The missing ingredient is an orderly mechanism for ensuring that all the daughter droplets receive the catalyst they need for all the reactions important to their survival. This is the pragmatic definition of the genetic apparatus . . ."[19]

"The evolution of the genetic machinery is the step for which there are no laboratory models. Hence, one can speculate endlessly, unfettered by inconvenient facts."[20]

Dickerson concludes that some form of energy direction is necessary:

"When it is finally understood exactly how the protein represser recognizes the base sequence of the DNA Operator, we may begin to hypothesize intelligently how a given sequence of bases could have produced a specific polypeptide chain sequence in the days before transfer RNA ribozones charging enzymes . . ."

"Through some gradual means, about which we can only now speculate, an association of nucleic acids as the archival material with protein as the working catalyst evolved into the complex genetic transcription and translation machinery that all forms of life exhibit today."[21] (emphasis added)

Conclusion

It is therefore concluded that neither the initiation of the universe nor the development of the complexity of the living system can be explained in terms of natural processes; for natural processes neither have the resources to finance the evolutionary development nor the intelligence to direct its progress. Initiation of elements from subatomic particles, or a pre-existent universe of hydrogen, requires as has been shown, enormous amounts of energy, as well as sophisticated energy ordering—negative entropy. The ordering process in the development of the elements of the atomic table is clearly evidenced in that all reactions postulated as a result of this initial "beginning" depend on the properties of those elements. Students at all levels are taught about the atomic table and the properties of the elements. Inorganic chemistry students study the principles of valence. Organic chemistry students study the constancy of bonding. Physical chemistry students study the order of the atomic structure through quantum mechanics. In fact, all these are areas of recognition of the existing order in the universe. Quantum mechanics clearly shows us the order in the atomic structure. It has been extremely useful in technological advances in solid state physics and in nuclear power generation. Such ordering is to be seen as a creative act. The only source for such a creative act, either at the beginning, or in the process of development of life, is a source outside the system itself or its surroundings. Indeed, a source "supernatural." In the final analysis, a scientific explanation based on natural processes as an explanation for the origin of the universe and the development of life is clearly stated by Dickerson as

"We can only imagine what probably existed, and our imagination so far has not been very helpful."[22]

On the other hand, an explanation based on a fully developed universe

50

with life in all its complex forms as a direct creative process of supernatural origin clearly fits in the observable data, and does no violence to the interpretation of current experiments or experiments on the origin of life and biological processes in general. In contrast, it provides a perspective for the examination of the world in which we live which is more than a "shot in the dark." It is a search for the unlimited capacity of the Creator to design and direct the universe, as the Biblical record indicates.

Appendix

(Excerpted from "Process Constraints in Living Systems",
Creation Research Society Journal 15(3):133

Therefore, let us consider life systems as processes. A typical process can be represented as

$$aA + bB \rightarrow cC + dD \tag{1}$$

This general expression relates reactants A and B to products C and D. (any number of reactants or products could be considered). The energies associated with the reactants and products are: internal energy, U, potential energy, X, kinetic energy, $v^2/2gc$ and pressure-volume energy, PV. The "system" can absorb heat, Q_i, from the surroundings and do work, W_s, on the surroundings. In addition, the system may be subjected to other work efforts, such as electrical, We, gravitational, W_g, magnetic, W_m, etc. If other than random work effects are present, appropriate additional terms must be included. Examples of non-random work are the separation of products, stacking a deck of cards, and the increase in system order in complex processes of life. Such processes require a work term, $-W_o$, to account for the work done on the system in directing the process outcome.

All of these energy terms can be included in a first law expression for the process represented by Equation 1. In general

$$dQ_i - dW_s = dE \tag{2}$$

51

where: Q_i = heat added to the system

      W_s = work done by the system is expansion or shaft work

      E = total energy of the system.

for open systems, the integral expression is

$$Q_i - W_s = E_2 - E_1 + \triangle U + \triangle PV + \triangle v^2/2g_c + \triangle X g/g_c \quad (3)$$

for steady flow $E_2 = E_1$ and only expansion or shaft work is considered,

$$Q_i - W_s = \triangle U + \triangle PV + \triangle v^2/2g_c + \triangle X g/g_c \quad (4)$$

where the other work effects are important, Equation 4 must be written as

$$Q_i - W_s = \triangle U + \triangle PV + \triangle v^2/2g_c + \triangle X g/g_c + W_e + W_g + W_m - W_o$$

since $U + PV = H$ (the enthalphy of the system) $\quad (5)$

$$Q_i - W_s = \triangle H + \triangle v^2/2g_c + \triangle X g/q_c + W_e + W_g + W_m - W_o \quad (6)$$

for systems where potential, kinetic, electromagnetic and gravity effects are negligible (life systems in general):

$$Q_i - W_s = \triangle H - W_o \quad (7)$$

and

$$Q_i = \triangle H + W_s - W_o \quad (8)$$

If the system or process is not doing expansion or shaft work on the surroundings, the term W_s is zero, and

$$Q_i = \triangle H - W_o \quad (9)$$

for such a system the second law expression for the entropy (S) change is

$$\triangle S_{TOT} = \int \frac{dQ}{T} \quad (10)$$

$$= \int \frac{d (\triangle H - W_o)}{T} \quad (11)$$

$$= \int \frac{dH}{T} - \frac{dW_o}{T} \quad (12)$$

$$= \triangle S_R - \triangle S_o \quad (13)$$

where: $\triangle S_{TOT}$ = total entropy change

      $\triangle S_R$ = entropy change due to random effects

      $\triangle S_o$ = entropy change due to increasing order

The expression for the change in entropy is, therefore, the sum of the change in entropy due to the chemical reaction $\int \frac{dH}{T}$ and the entropy change due to the increase in order or information in the system, $\triangle S_o$.

Equations 12 and 13 are useful in explaining complex processes having both random and non-random character. As an example, crystallization takes place partially by well defined change of state heat effects which are reversible and purely random. The crystal formation, however, is not random, and the atoms deposit themselves in a specific order. This order is so precise that many very sophisticated analytical techniques depend on crystalline structures being *exactly* ordered. The entropy associated with the random cooling process and the heat of crystallization are quantitatively measured by the first term on the right hand size of Eq. 12. The non-random part of the process, or the ordering of the crystal, is represented by the second term on the right of Eq. 12. It cannot be quantitatively measured for it represents the information contained in the atomic structure of the atom species. The second term effect is, however, clearly evident in the regularity of the crystal!

Equation 13 is helpful in analyazing processes in which chemical effects are negligible and probability effects prominent. As an example, the process of "stacking" a deck of cards as opposed to a random "shuffle" involves $- W_o$ only and

$$\triangle S_{TOT} = O - \triangle S_o \qquad (14)$$

In this case the $- \triangle S_o$ can be calculated from probability theory since

$$S = k \ln p \qquad (15)$$

where: $p =$ the probability of the "stacked" order
$k =$ Boltzman constant

It should be emphasized that the two entropy terms in Eq. 13 result from different "types" of energy transfer, and the interchange of energy between the system and its surroundings in terms of entropy exchange must be of the same "kind". The argument that an "open" system will provide the necessary entropy sink for life systems is erroneous. The decrease in entropy due to increasing order cannot be financed by an increase in entropy in the sun or in any other random process in the surroundings. It can only be financed by energy from an equivalent "quality" source.

This can be illustrated by considering a process of putting a watch together. If the parts of a watch were arrayed on a table "opening" the system to the sun, or to the universe for that matter, would not be effec-

53

tive in making a watch. Only the application of a certain "kind" of energy—intelligence or ordered energy—could do it. And, of course, we know that is just what happens. The watchmaker provides the $-W_o$ energy work on the system in accord with Equation 9. The introduction of the $-W_o$ term into Eq. 8 does not apriori imply a Creator. It does imply a certain kind of operation that must take place. The term, having been introduced, could be omitted once the proper understanding of energy interchange is achieved. Evolutionary theory claims that the term $-W_o$ is a result of natural selection, random chance, and long time spans. Creation theory claims that $-W_o$ comes from supernatural causes.

REFERENCES

[1]Wald, George 1955. The origin of life in The Physics and chemistry of life. Simon and Schuster, New York, p.12.

[2]Weisskopf, V.F. 1977. The frontiers and limits of science. *American Scientist* 65(4):405.

[3]Prigogine, I., G. Nicolis, and A. Babylontz. 1971. Thermodynamics of evolution. *Physics Today* 25 (11):23.

[4]Brillouin, L. 1949. Life, thermodynamics and cybernetics. *American Scientist* 37(10):554-5.

[5]Boylan, D.R. 1978. Process constraints in living systems. *Creation Reserch Society Quarterly* 15(3):133.

[6]Schrodinger, Edwin. 1956. What is life? Doubleday, New York. p. 71.

[7]Calvin, Melvin, 1975. Chemical evolution. *American Scientist* 63(2):169.

[8]*Ibid.*, p. 171.

[9]*Ibid.*

[10]Cloud, Preston, 1977. Scientific creation - a new inquisition. *The Humanist XXXVII (1):15.*

[11]Boylan, *Op Cit.*

[12]Quinn, L.Y. 1975. The evidence for the existence of an intelligible genetic code. *Creation Reserach Society Quarterly* 11(4):196-7.

[13]Stull, D.R. 1971. The thermodynamic transformation of organic chemistry. *American Scientist* 59(6):734.

[14]Dickerson, R.E. 1978. Chemical evolution and the origin of life. *Scientific American* 239(9):73.

[15]*Ibid.*

[16]*Ibid.*

[17]*Ibid.*, p. 78.

[18]*Ibid.*

[19]*Ibid.*

[20]*Ibid.*, p. 85.

[21]*Ibid.*, p. 86.

[22]*Ibid.*

3

Fluctuations As A Mechanism Of Ordering

Emmett L. Williams

Introduction

The introduction of the concept of fluctuations has been heralded as the possible driving force for evolution.[1] As stated by Prigogine, Nicolis, and Babloyantz,

> For reasons to be explained later, we shall refer to this principle as order through fluctuations.[2]

Obviously the scientific world considered the work to be of such importance that Ilya Prigogine was awarded a Nobel Prize in 1977 for his efforts.

The entire subject falls within the domain of irreversible thermodynamics and the arguments must be evaluated thermodynamically. An interested reader may find a comprehensive development of the thermodynamics of structure and fluctuations in reference 3. For a creationist interpretation of irreversible thermodynamics, see reference 4.

Unrealistic Starting Conditions

It is well-known that all entities in the inorganic world proceed toward a state of equilibrium fairly rapidly. The attainment of equilibrium is much slower in living systems[5] but is still evident.

Thus to model his systems as close to "the desires of nature" as possible, an evolutionist should start the molecules-to-man process at an equilibrium state and work "upward." However upon investigation of many evolutionary schemes from astronomy to biology, it is found that the usual initial state is one of nonequilibrium. Evolutionists need pre-existing order to provide any hope of success in their hypothesized process since the equilibrium state is one of maximum disorder.[6]

As for the first law of thermodynamics, order can bring forth more order.[7] For example, living systems can replicate themselves. Therefore a nonequilibrium state is no proper place to start any molecules-to-man scheme; since the biggest problem has been avoided, getting the system out of the equilibrium state, while all known natural "forces" want to maintain that condition. Nonequilibrium states are entirely unrealistic as starting points for molecules-to-man evolution. This very assumpton completely voids the idea as a sensible theory of origins.

The work of Prigogine et al. deals totally with nonequilibrium states. The main idea is the possibility that a prebiological system may evolve through a whole succession of transitions leading to a hierarchy of more and more complex and organized states. Such transitions can only arise in nonlinear systems that are maintained far from equilibrium: that is, beyond a certain critical threshold the steady-state regime becomes unstable and the system evolves to a new configuration.[8]

The subject of origins is beyond the scope of the concept and this is admitted by the authors.

This picture of selection through "survival of the fittest" already implies the existence of self-maintaining and self-reproducing systems. Strictly speaking therefore, it is not a theory of the origin of life.[9]

When the work is carefully investigated it is found that it is not a proper basis for evolution.

Dissipative Structures
To maintain the artificial nonequilibrium state, even in theory, a number of imaginary structures must be invented.

As might be expected, the stability of thermodynamic equilibrium implies the stability of states near equilibrium. This is the reason why all non-trivial stability problems cannot be approached by linear thermodynamics of irreversible processes. The possibility of new types of organization of matter past an instability point under the influence of non-equilibrium conditions, occurs only when the system is sufficiently far from equilibrium. The study of such a new organization, the so-called dissipative structure, arising from the exchange of matter and energy with the outside world, appears as one of the most fascinating subjects of mascroscopic physics.[10]

The equilibrium state can be defined away if one invents a dissipative structure which has as its sole purpose the ability to reject entropy faster than it can produce or receive it! Then order can be maintained and useful information can be transferred between structures.

Such a construct has definite advantages.

It is therefore possible, a priori, to have a number of new effects, for instance: the system may not decay monotonically to the steady state belonging to the thermodynamic branch, once it is perturbed from it; in the limit it may even never return to this state but evolve to a time-dependent regime: under similar conditions it may finally deviate and evolve to a new stationary regime corresponding to a branch different from the thermodynamic one. This transition will manifest itself abruptly as an instability, i.e. as a fundamentally discontinuous process.[11]

Since the entropy of an isolated system is a monotonically increasing function of time,[12] dissipative structures are a very neat way of avoiding the degenerating influences in nature. In the marriage of kinetics with thermodynamics to form the science of irreversible thermodynamics, the tail (kinetics) has begun to wag the dog (thermodynamics).[13] The system under study is conveniently kept away from equilibrium by theoretical dissipative structures.

It is therefore very tempting to associate biological structures with thermal instabilities leading to a spontaneous self-organization.[14]

Once the imagined system gets far enough away from equilibrium, order spontaneously generates!

Summarizing, we may say that instabilities in the thermodynamic branch of solutions can lead to time or space organization and to a change in functional behavior in open systems undergoing chemical reactions.[15]

The creation of order by virtue of instabilities is an example of imagined ever-onward-upward evolution.

It would be thus very tempting to think that dissipative instabilities act as a kind of phase transition leading to a new state of matter.[16]

This new state of matter is one in which the second law of thermodynamics has been overcome. At last the evolutionist has triumped over observable phenomena.

It is exciting to realize that the analogy between dissipative and biological structures may lead to the idea that life and absence of life are just two states of matter separated by a chemical instability.[17]

Thus a totally atheistic, mechanistic, and naturalistic picture of life has evolved from the consideration of dissipative structures. Such structures may be excellent models for studying the maintenance of existing nonequilibrium living systems, but they cannot explain how these systems originated.

Order Through Fluctuations

The general path supposedly taken by fluctuations and dissipative structures is that of higher and higher order. Such a process can be visualized in Figure 1.

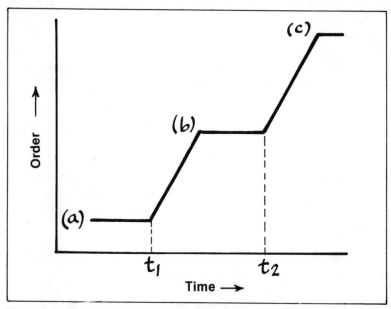

Figure 1 Schematic diagram of an increase in order by fluctuations and stabilization of the order by conservation processes

A nonequilibrium state (a) exists and is made stable by conservation processes. Suddenly a system fluctuation at time t_1 drives it to a more highly-ordered state (b). This state is stabilized for a while by conservation processes until another fluctuation occurs at time t_2 driving the system to an even more highly ordered state (c). This state is made stable by conservation processes, and the net system ordered has increased by such imagined processes.

It should be noted that when fluctuations of the right kind are needed, they occur. When conservation processes are needed, they operate. When thermodynamic considerations (conservation) need to be overcome, kinetics (fluctuations) can do the job. You systematically allow for what you want to happen. It is unfortunate that nature is not that cooperative with evolutionary necessity. Yet fluctuations and conservation processes seem never to interfere with each other and degeneration processes seem reluctant to act! Evolution by "blessed events"[18] can operate.

The seemingly perfect working-together of fluctuations and conservation processes are totally unnatural. These changes exist only in the minds of evolutionary scientists. Men can intelligently plan and cause changes that apparently lower the entropy of a system. Constant maintenance of the system at a low entropy state by energy inflow and outflow is necessary to hold back the degenerating effects. Yet eventually even the preservation processes of the ordered open system coupled to its surroundings cannot stop the degeneration.[19] It appears that God has created into the living organisms certain conservation processes that slow down the inevitable, yet the state of maximum entropy or disorder is eventually reached.[20, 21]

If thermodynamic principles were left free to perform in the naturally-expected manner, the net result of the fluctuation process might be as follows. The original created order state (a) in Figure 2 is

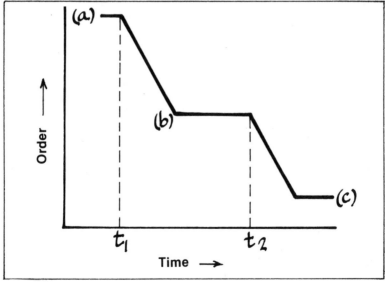

Figure 2 Schematic diagram of a decrease in order by fluctuations and stabilization of the order by conservation processes

stabilized by conservation processes. A fluctuation occurs at time t_1 driving the system to a new metastable state (b) of lower order. Conservation processes maintain state (b) until another fluctuation occurs at time t_2 driving the system to state (c) of even lowered order. This type of behavior would be expected with the interaction of conservation and degeneration processes.[22]

At best the level of ordering expected in the interaction of conservation and degeneration processes[23] is shown in Figure 3. The original created order is shown as state (a). The same fluctuation-conservation-degeneration pattern is seen at states (b) and (c) and at times t_1 and t_2 as shown in Figure 2. However at time t_3 a fluctuation causes the system to change to state (d) which is more ordered than states (b) or (c). Such an ordering process can be imagined as long as it results in a state with less order than (a). No change or fluctuaton can generate more order than the original state (in this case the created order). Possibly such a change is a model of what occurs in genetic recombination. A further change noted in Figure 3 fluxes the system at time t_4 from state (d) to a state (e) of lower order.

It would seem that the postulated changes illustrated in Figure 2 and 3 provide a more realistic model for natural situations. Order can bring forth other order (conservation processes) but order can never arise spontaneously out of disorder (equilibrium state).

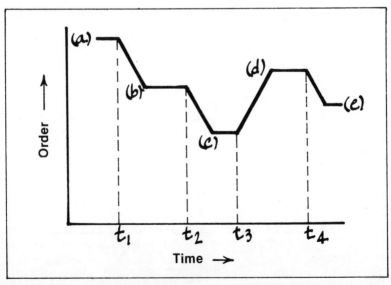

Figure 3 Interaction of fluctuations, conservation and degeneration processes to produce temporary order

Do fluctuations honestly lead to states of higher order? This question was asked of Prigogine.[24]

J. Keck: I would like to comment on Professor Prigogine's remarks about generation of order from disorder.

What you have described to us was the decay of a metastable state into a more ordered state. In the same sense, an explosion would be an example in which a degree of order is created out of disorder by releasing energy.

I wonder if you would make a distinction between your example and mine. I don't really think these are examples of the creation of order out of disorder. The systems were metastable to begin with.

I. Prigogine: The order to which I referred corresponds to situations which are sufficiently far from thermodynamic equilibrium, and which permits to transform the flow of energy into structure.

We go then from our branch of the solution of the conservation equation to another branch.

The above exchange lays bare the inadequacy of the evolutionary schemes. Order is not created out of disorder. If an explosion in a print factory can generate Webster's Unabridged Dictionary, then molecules-to-man evolution can occur by the proposed fluctuation mechanism.

Fluctuations at Equilibrium

Essentially for fluctuations to be of importance in the evolutionary hypothesis of origins, they must be able to bring a system out of equilibrium state into a stable nonequilibrium state. This concept will be developed using fluctuations in entropy of an ideal monatomic gas system at equilibrium for simplicity. An ideal gas at known temperature, pressure, and volume is considered a macrostate. The actual arrangement of the atoms at this state cannot be observed; however statistical considerations can be introduced as a model for what is happening on the atomic level.

The atoms of gas are in constant motion in a state of disorder. Yet if it were possible to take a photograph each instant, the positions of the atoms in one photograph would be different from their positions in other photographs. Yet each would be of a disordered arrangement. These would represent various microstates of the system, and make up all of the possible arrangements of the equilibrium macrostate designated by W_e. Suppose a fluctuation causes the atoms in the gas to assume a slightly ordered arrangement. This new macrostate is represented by W_{ne} since it is a nonequilibrium condition.

The entropy change in going from one macrostate to another can be calculated using the Boltzmann formula as follows.[25]

$$dS = k \ln \frac{W_{ne}}{W_e} \tag{1}$$

where $dS = S_{ne} - S_e$, S_{ne} = entropy of the nonequilibrium state, S_e = entropy of the equilibrium state, and k is Boltzmann's constant. Starting with the first law of thermodynamics for an ideal gas

$$dU = dQ + dW \tag{2}$$

where dU = internal energy gained or lost by the system, dQ = heat gained or lost by the system, dW = work done on or by system, $dW = -PdV$ (mechanical work only), P = pressure of gas, and V = volume of gas.

Thus (2) becomes

$$dU = dQ - PdV \tag{3}$$

From the classical definition of the change in entropy, $dS = dQ/T$. T is the absolute temperature; Equation 3 becomes $dU = TdS - PdV$,

$$\text{or} \quad dS = \frac{dU}{T} + \frac{PdV}{T} \tag{4}$$

The internal energy of an ideal gas is a function of temperature only so that $dU = C_v dT$. Also $C_v = 3R/2$. Here R is the ideal gas constant. Therefore Equation 4 after substitution can be written as

$$dS = \frac{3}{2} \frac{R}{T} \frac{dT}{T} + \frac{P}{T} dV \tag{4'}$$

By the ideal gas law $PV = nRT$, or $P/T = nR/V$, where n = number of moles of gas, then

$$dS = \frac{3}{2} \frac{R}{T} \frac{dT}{T} + \frac{nRdV}{V} dV \tag{5}$$

Indefinite integration of Equation 5 yields

$$S = \frac{3}{2} R \ln T + nR \ln V + S_o \tag{6}$$

where S_o is the integration constant.

If $n = 1$, then $nR = Nk$. Here N is Avogadro's number; and Equation 6 becomes[26]

$$S = Nk(\ln VT^{3/2} + \frac{S_o}{R}). \qquad (7)$$

This equation represents the entropy of one mole of an ideal monatomic gas at temperature T and volume V.

$$S = NkC$$

$$\text{where } C = (\ln VT^{3/2} + \frac{S_0}{R}) \qquad (8)$$

Return to Equation 1. When the fluctuation occurs the entropy decreases since $W_e > W_{ne}$ and dS is negative.[27]

Equation 8 can be written as

$$dS = NkCx \qquad (9)$$

where x is the fractional decrease in entropy due to the fluctuation.

Equate Equations 1 and 9:

$$\frac{W_{ne}}{W_e} = e^{-NCx} = e^{-NCx}$$

If the gas is assumed to be helium at 273°K and 1 atm., [28] C = 14.96, and

$$W_{ne}/W_e = e^{-15Nx}.$$

Suppose an entropy decrease of one part in a million occurs as a result of the fluctuations, or $x = 10^{-6}$, then $N = 6.02 \times 10^{23}$; and $15Nx \approx 10^{19}$, or $W_{ne}/W_e = e^{-10^{19}} (2.7)^{-10^{19}}$.

Thus the chance of an infinitesimally small entropy decrease is about 10 raised to the -10^{19} power.[29] The odds against any sizeable entropy decrease would be astronomical. Fluctuations offer no hope to the evolutionist to drive a system out of an equilibrium state.

Even if minute ordering fluctuations do occur somewhere in the system, immediately upon another fluctuation the short-range would be destroyed. Another area of order may appear simultaneously in some other part of the system. Yet it will be dissipated by the next fluctuation.

The process can be schematically represented in Figure 4. The macroscopic entropy of the system does not change. However during system fluctuations, short-range order can develop, dissipate, develop, elsewhere, dissipate, etc. A fluctuation occurs at t_1 causing the appearance of short-range order. Another fluctuation at time t_2 causes the order to dissipate in that area. No lasting order can be built up by such a process. Molecules-to-man evolution needs ordering fluctuations of

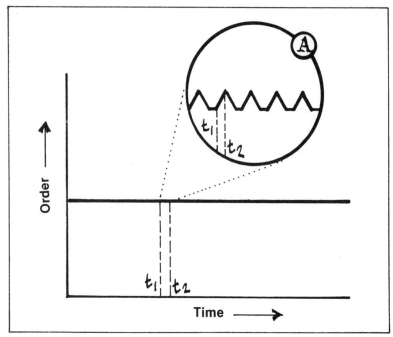

Figure 4 The production of short-range order in a gaseous system subject to fluctuations at equilibrium. Insert A represents a small section of the curve greatly magnified; it shows how the curve of order vs. time may be "bumpy" due to microscopic fluctuations.

monumental magnitude and unnatural locking mechanisms to stabilize any generated order as degenerative forces attempt to drive the system back to equilibrium. Such schemes can be created on paper, but the operation of them in nature is doubtful.

Such a hopeless procedure appears to be doomed to failure. The primary need of any evolutionary hypothesis — to move the system away from equilibrium — is highly improbable. Actually fluctuations tend to disorder a system,[30] and if the improbable does happen on one fluctuation, the probable will occur in succeeding fluctuations destroying any temporary order.

Conclusions

Although there are fluctuations in natural systems such as shock waves and other catastrophic events, it is unreasonable to assume that they can be used as a driving force for molecules-to-man evolution. Nonuniform conditions can exist briefly as illustrated by the Zhabotinski reaction.[31] However, like all real systems, it is driven toward equilibrium and does not proceed to higher states of order. Dissipative structures offer considerable promise as good models for living systems and certain temporary nonequilibrium states found in nature. However they cannot be used as models for the origin of such systems. The major problem that must be faced by evolutionists is how their imagined universe moved out of the preferred natural state of equilibrium. Natural means seem fruitless. The writer prefers to believe

In the beginning God created the heaven and the earth as the origin of natural order.

REFERENCES

[1]Prigogine, I., Nicolis, G. and Babloyantz, A., 1972 Thermodynamics of evolution. *Physics Today* 25(11):23-28; 25(12):38-44.

[2]*Ibid*. pg. 25.

[3]Glansdorff, P., and Prigogine, I., 1971. Thermodynamic theory of structure, stability and fluctuations. Wiley-Interscience, New York.

[4]Williams, E. L., 1971. Resistance of living organisms to the second law of thermodynamics; irreversible processes, open systems, creation and evolution. *Creation Research Society Quarterly* 8(2):117-126.

[5]*Ibid*.

[6]Williams, E.L., 1966. Entropy and the solid state. *Creation Research Society Quarterly* 3(3):18-24.

[7]Williams, 1971. *Op cit*.

[8]Prigogine, Nicolis, and Babloyantz, 1972. *Op cit*., pg. 25.

[9]*Ibid*., pg. 38.

[10]Glansdorff and Prigogine. *Op cit*., pg. 73.

[11]Nicolis, G., 1970. Thermodynamic theory of stability, structure, and fluctuations. *Pure and Applied Chemistry* 22(3-4):388.

[12]Williams, E.L., 1973. Thermodynamics: a tool for creationists (review of recent literature). *Creation Research Society Quarterly* 10(1):38-44.

[13]Williams, 1971. *Op cit*., pgs. 117, 119, 121.

[14]Nicolis, *Op cit*.., pg. 390.

[15]Nicolis, *Ibid*.

[16]Nicolis, *Ibid*., pg. 391.

[17]Nicolis, *Ibid*.

[18]Williams, E. L., 1967. The evolution of complex organic compounds from simpler chemical compounds: is it thermodynamically and kinetically possible? *Creation Research Society Quarterly* 4(1):30-35. See especially p. 34.

[19]Williams, E. L., 1969. A simplified explanation of the first and second laws of thermodynamics: their relationship to scripture and the theory of evolution. *Creation Research Society Quarterly* 5(4):138-147. See especially p. 145.

[20]Williams, 1971. *Op cit*.

[21]Williams, E. L., 1974. Living organisms: conservation and degeneration processes. A Challenge to Education: Technical Essays. Second Creation Convention, Milwaukee, August 18-21, 1974, Bible Science Association, Caldwell, Idaho II B:103-113.

[22]Williams, E. L., 1976. A creation model for natural processes. *Creation Research Society Quarterly* 13(1):34-37. See especially p. 36.

[23]Williams, E. L., 1977. Living systems - conservation and degeneration. A Challenge to Biology. Fifth Annual Creation Convention at the Philadelphia College of Bible, August 14-17, Bible Science Association, Caldwell, Idaho: 13-14.

[24]Panel Discussion 1970. A critical review of thermodynamics edited by E. B. Stuart, B. Gal-Or, and A. J. Brainard-Mono Book Corp. Baltimore: 205-206.

[25]Williams, E. L., 1966. *Op cit.*

[26]Crawford, F. H. 1963. Heat, thermodynamics and statistical physics. Harcourt, Brace, and World, Inc. New York. 518-520.

[27]Williams, 1966. *Op. cit.*, p. 20.

[28]Crawford, *Op. cit.*, p. 519.

[29]*Ibid.*, p. 520.

[30]Williams, 1973. *Op cit.*, p. 42.

[31]Glansdorff and Prigogine, 1971. *Op cit.*, pp. 261-263.

4

The Origin of Biological Order
and the Second Law

Duane T. Gish

Evolution Model: Problems

Evolutionists, as part of an evolutionary continuum, postulate a mechanistic, naturalistic, evolutionary origin of life on this planet. Let us first of all consider the immensity of the problem. This evolutionary scenario begins with a primordial earth containing simple gases in its atmosphere, including methane, ammonia, hydrogen, nitrogen, water vapor, carbon monoxide, ammonia, hydrogen, nitrogen, water vapor, carbon dioxide, and minor amounts of other gases. Most of the available energy would have been supplied by the sun, with a minor amount provided by electrical discharges, and much lesser and thermodynamically insignificant amounts being provided from radioactive decay, heat, etc. The scenario includes barren land masses surrounded by the primordial oceans, with temperatures not greatly different from those of today.

A billion years or so later, according to the generally accepted scenario, the ocean was swarming with microscopic, single-celled forms of life. What was this postulated primordial form of life like? What would have been required of the most primitive form of life imaginable? No one really knows, of course, but of this we can be certain—it would have been tremendously complicated. The simplest form of life imaginable would require at the very least several hundreds, and most likely, several thousands of different kinds of large and complex molecules, such as proteins, DNA, and RNA. Concerning this point, Van Rensselaer Potter has said, "It is possible to hazard a guess that the number is not less than 1,000, but whether it is 3,000 or 10,000 or greater is anyone's guess."[1] Potter's statement certainly acknowledges the immense complexity of the postulated primordial cell while at the same time tactly admitting how little is really known or knowable about this hypothetical entity.

Of course a living cell is more than just a bag of chemicals. It requires a membrane, and membranes of living cells are very complex in structure and dynamic in function. Found within cells are many complex structures, such as microsomes, ribosomes, mitochondria (or energy-producing complexes of some kind), Golgi bodies, etc.

Furthermore, life requires marvelous coordination in time and space, with many regulatory mechanisms. In comparing living cells to simple abiogenic systems, Oparin stated, "However, living systems differ fundamentally from all such open systems in the orderly regulation of their metabolism and the 'purposefulness' of their internal structure. Not only are the many tens and hundreds of thousands of chemical reactions which occur in protoplams, and which together constitute its metabolism, strictly coordinated with one another in time, harmoniously composed in a single series of processes which constantly repeat themselves, but the whole series is directed towards a single goal, toward the uninterrupted self-preservation and self-reproducton of the living system as a whole in accordance with the conditions of the surrounding medium."[2]

Green and Goldberger have said, ". . . the macromolecule to cell transition is a jump of fantastic dimensions, which lies beyond the range of testable hypothesis. In this area all is conjecture. The available facts do not provide a basis for postulating that cells arose on this planet."[3]

Finally, let us attempt to visualize the complexity of a single-celled organism by considering the probability of matter existing in such an arrangement. By adding up the energy content of all the chemical bonds in a "simple" bacterium and comparing this to the energy content at equilibrium of the constitutent atoms from which it was formed, Morowitz[4] calculated the probability of this cell to be $10^{-10^{11}}$. That is a probability of one out of the number one followed by 100 billion zeroes! This latter number is so large it would take about 100 thousand volumes of 500 pages each just to print.

Perhaps now we can grasp the immensity of the problem. According to the evolutionary scenario, matter started on this planet in the form of simple gases which transformed themselves by spontaneous, naturally occurring processes into the immensely complex entity called a living cell—all of this in spite of a universal natural tendency to go in exactly the opposite direction!

Natural Processes

Let us now review the natural tendency of matter concerning self-transformation. R. B. Lindsay has said "There is a natural tendency of all observed systems to go from order to disorder, reflecting dissipation of energy available for future transformation—the law of increasing entropy."[5]

Harold Blum stated, "All real processes go with an increase of entropy. The entropy also measures the randomness, or lack of orderliness of the system. The greater the randomness, the greater the entropy."[6]

Isaac Asimov has put it this way, "'Another way of stating the second law then is 'The universe is constantly getting more disorderly!' Viewed that way we can see the second law all about us. We have to work hard to straighten a room, but left to itself it becomes a mess again very quickly and very easily. Even if we never enter it, it becomes dusty and musty. How difficult to maintain houses, and machinery, and our own bodies in perfect working order: how easy to let them deteriorate. In fact, all we have to do is nothing, and everything deteriorates, collapses, breaks down, wears out, all by itself—and that is what the second law is all about.'"[7]

All right, then, *that* is what the second law is all about—everything tends to deteriorate, all observed systems exhibit a natural tendency to go from order to disorder, all real processes go with an increase in entropy, the entropy measuring the randomness, or lack of orderliness of the system. This is what we observe out there in the real world. This tendency is universal. It applies to *all* systems, open or closed. The *tendency* is *always* to go from order to disorder.

We see this all-pervasive natural tendency at every level of organization, from the atom to the universe. Clusters of galaxies are dispersing and becoming more randomly arranged; clusters of stars are breaking up; stars explode in supernovas and all stars, including our sun, are burning up as their fuel is being exhausted; the rotation of the earth is slowing; the magnetic field of the earth is decaying; mountains erode; houses inevitably fall apart; automobiles deteriorate; our bodies age; bacteria age and die; even certain atoms decay radioactively. Nothing is exempt. The cost is staggering. Billions and billions of dollars are spent each year in maintenance and upkeep, repairs, painting, replacement of parts, medical bills, funerals.

This all-pervasive natural tendency, unless God intervenes, will eventually overwhelm the entire universe, and all life, all activity, will cease as all energy sources are exhausted. Even the law of increasing entropy will cease to be a law as entropy reaches a maximum.

It matters little whether we call this natural tendency a law or not. It matters not at all whether or not in the present universe there are local and temporary complex and specialized systems in which order and complexity can be caused to increase in spite of the tendency to go in the opposite direction. The *tendency* in natural, spontaneously occurring processes is *always* to go from order to disorder, from complexity to simplicity. Every part of the universe, from atoms to galaxies, *tend* to go in that direction. The universe itself inexorably, moment by moment, is moving in that direction. No system escapes.

What more can we say to emphasize that every particle, every atom, in every part of the natural universe, as far as scientists have been able to determine, is subject to this natural tendency? It is obvious, on the other hand, that there is *no* tendency on the part of matter to organize itself and to spontaneously transform itself into higher and higher levels of organization.

Necessary Ordering Force

Let us now go back and consider once again what evolutionists believe has occurred on this planet by spontaneous, naturally occurring processes. Simple gases, such as methane, ammonia, hydrogen, and water vapor, have transformed themselves in the presence of highly destructive energy sources, such as ultraviolet light and electrical discharges, into incredibly complex living cells. According to evolutionists, this was a progressive process that inexorably transformed matter to higher and higher levels of organization until finally the living cell arose—the most complex, the most unstable arrangement of matter in the universe—an arrangement of matter so improbable that the probability of its existence in that state compared to its existence as simple matter at equilibrium is $10^{-10^{11}}$.

It is immediately obvious to anyone who is willing to give the problem careful consideration, unburdened by any philosophical necessities, that if life has indeed evolved, there must have been some extremely powerful organizing force or principle at work. Something had to be *imposed* upon the system to overcome the overwhelming, all pervasive natural tendency for every part of the system every moment to go in exactly the opposite direction. It is incumbent upon those who suggest that life on the earth arose spontaneously through abiogenesis to demonstrate what that powerful organizing principle could have been.

Certainly the simple expenditure of energy would not be sufficient. In fact, raw uncontrolled energy is destructive, not constructive. Simpson and Beck have said ". . . the simple expenditure of energy is not sufficient to develop and maintain order. A bull in a china shop performs work, but he neither creates nor maintains organization. The work needed is *particular* work; it must follow specifications; it requires information on how to proceed."[8] Simpson and Beck are both advocates of an evolutionary origin of life, but neither actually have any alternative to what amounts to a "bull in a china shop" idea to explain the origin of life.

Wrighton states, "Running a chemical reaction uphill is a tricky business. To produce thermodynamically unstable mixtures that can be stored indefinitely, kinetic barriers to back reaction (reversion to starting materials) must be built into the fuel production mechanism to prevent the premature release of energy."[9] Since running a chemical reaction uphill is indeed a tricky business (and every step in the origin of life would be going uphill, thermodynamically), certainly the simple expenditure of energy will not suffice to explain the origin of biological order.

Harold Blum, totally devoted to a mechanistic origin of life, states, "The temperature of the sun is near 6,000 degrees K, that of the earth about 285 degrees K. Energy flows from the former to the latter with an accompanying increase in entropy, and a *suitable machine* can convert into work some of the energy flowing from the hot to the cold body"[10] (emphasis added). Blum, as do all other advocates of an evolutionary origin of life, maintains that the second law of thermodynamics poses no problem to the evolutionary origin of life on the earth because the earth is an open system and receives energy from the sun. Here, as noted, however, Blum rightly interposes the necessity of a suitable machine. A thorough search of Blum's book reveals that he has certainly not been able to suggest what that suitable machine was.

Thermodynamics and Kinetics of Ordering

Let us now consider the application of thermodynamic processes to the origin of relatively simple organic chemical molecules. The first prerequisite for an abiogenic origin of life would be the generation of huge quantities of such necessary monomers as amino acids, certain sugars, purines, pyrimidines and a host of other molecules vital to the origin of life. The oceans contain about 350 million cubic miles of water. Any mechanism one might conceive to locally concentrate organic substance could only operate temporarily, and thus any compound so concentrated would soon be washed out to sea and diluted in the 350 million cubic miles of water. Any substance that would reach a significant concentration (0.01- 0.1 molar) must thus be produced in quantities of many billions of tons. An efficient method for producing the required organic molecules must therefore have been operating on the primitive earth.

Hull has published a concise but informative treatment of the problem of generating these substances under presumed primitive earth conditions.[11] Based upon a quantum yield for the decarboxylation of activated glycine of the order of unity, the absorption coefficient of glycine, and the intensity of ultraviolet radiation below 3000 angstroms, Hull calculated a half-life of glycine in the atmosphere of about 30 days. Since the half-time of transport from the stratosphere to the surface of the ocean is about three years, 97% of the glycine produced in the atmosphere would be destroyed before reaching the ocean. Even after reaching the ocean, destruction continues, due mainly to the penetration of the upper layer of the ocean by ultraviolet light. Even making the extreme assumption that the glycine would be mixed to the bottom of the ocean, its half-life would only be about 1000 years.

A limiting concentration of glycine under assumed primitive earth conditions can be estimated for steady state conditions by comparing rates of production and decomposition. Using an assumed quantum yield for glycine under these conditions of 10^{-6} (based on the experimental work of others), and allowing for 3 percent to reach the ocean and a 1000-year half-life there, Hull calculated a maximum molar concentration in the sea for glycine to be 10^{-12}. Even this concentration would be hopelesly low for origin of life schemes, but the actual concentration would more likely be between the steady state concentration of 10^{-12} and the thermodynamic concentration of 10^{-27}.

Glycine is the simplest of the amino acids, containing only two carbon atoms. The situation becomes progressively much worse thermodynamically as more complex organic compounds are considered. As compounds become more complex, their rates of formation decrease drastically while their rates of destruction increase sharply. This is so because while the quantum yield for their formation decreases, their stability to thermal decomposition decreases and their opacity to ultraviolet light and destruction by this means increases. The calculated equilibrium concentration of glucose, for example, a six-carbon sugar, is 10^{-134} molar. That concentration is so low, that it would be difficult to find a single molecule in the entire universe!

Hull concludes, ''The physical chemist guided by the proved principles of chemical thermodynamics and kinetics, cannot offer any encouragement to the biochemist, who needs an ocean full of organic compounds to form even lifeless coacervates . . . The second law of thermodynamics applies not only to inorganic gases in the atmosphere, but also to organic compounds in the ocean. Living cells may reverse the process, but in the absence of life, 'die Entropie der Welt strebt einem Maximum zu.' ''

Considering the fact that, as Hull has emphasized, greater complexity decreases stability rather than enhancing it, Blum's attempts to wrestle with the evolution of life and the second law produces surprising results at some points. Blum asks,[12] ''If all things tend continually toward a condition of greater randomness, which would seem to represent a tendency toward increasing uniformity, how can complexity increase in even small parts of a system?'' He then goes on to explain that the rate of flow of events in that direction (of increasing entropy) is not uniform, some events moving more rapidly than others in the direction of greater randomness, and that with different processes going at different rates, greater apparent complexity may result during finite periods of time and within restricted areas of the system.

Now that is indeed a unique solution to the problem of the origin of biological order and the second law! All things do rush toward greater disorder, but some things rush faster than others, and those that get left behind have greater apparent complexity—and that explains the origin of order and complexity! Two flaws, among others, in this sort of reasoning immediately suggest themselves. In the first place, how did things get in a complex, low entropy state, away from which they have moved, supposedly, at varying rates, thus generating apparent complexity? Furthermore, the more complex an organic molecule or system is, the more unstable it is. Thus, the more complex the system or molecule, the faster it would move toward greater disorder. Blum's suggested solution is thus no solution at all. At least we can thank him for restating the problem, for indeed if all things tend continually toward a condition of greater randomness, how *can* complexity increase in even small parts of the system?

We have seen that even at the stage of relatively simple organic molecules, the universal tendency toward disorder would prevent the accumulation of significant quantities of these substances. This tendency results in the well-established principle that rates of destruction of these products vastly exceed their rates of formation. Thus the interplay of a sufficient quantity of highly energetic quanta of energy with certain gases will produce amino acids. For example,

$$2CH_4 + NH_3 + 2H_2O \rightleftharpoons H_2NCH_2COOH + H_2O$$

Since the equilibrium constant for the above reaction is 2×10^{-40}, no amino acid will be produced, for all practical purposes, without the addition of energy. If, however, the gases are irradiated with ultraviolet light, the radiant energy initially tends to drive the reaction toward the right, and some molecules of amino acids are produced. The glycine molecules (and other amno acids) produced, however, are immediately vulnerable to radiation. Furthermore, these molecules absorb radiation up to 3000 angstroms, a portion of the solar spectrum far more intense than that portion of shorter wavelength that produced them.

The result, as mentioned earlier, is a production rate of glycine with a quantum yield of 10^{-6} (one molecule of glycine would be produced for every million quanta of energy absorbed by the gas molecules), and a destruction rate with a quantum yield of unity (every molecule of glycine which absorbs a quantum of energy is destroyed by spontaneous decarboxylaton). The overall net result is that no significant quantity of product is synthesized. The same final result would be obtained if we started with a high concentration of amino acids and the gases. The amino acids would be rapidly destroyed while insignificant quantities are produced from the gases. Eventually the quantity of amino acids would be reduced to the level obtained in the first experiment. No matter from which direction we proceed, the results are fully in accord with those predicted on the basis of the second law.

Laboratory Experiments

How, then, was Stanley Miller successful in obtaining a detectable quantity of amino acids by subjecting a mixture of gases to an electrical discharge?[13] Why have similar experiments succeeded in producing quantities of other products? They have simply employed a trap of some kind to selectively remove the products from the reaction vessel. Chemists commonly employ such devices to increase the yields of desired products. The second law is not violated, of course. The chemist has merely imposed his ingenuity and devices on nature to circumvent the direction it would ordinarily go.

Unfortunately, there were no chemists on the hypothetical primordial earth to supply the trap, and no natural trap has yet been discovered. More importantly, even the trap, if one existed, would be fatal to origin of life schemes. If products are trapped to remove them from the energy source that produced them, thus preserving them from destruction, no further movement in the direction of the origin of life would be possible. Every step in the origin of life would be an uphill process, requiring a very considerable expenditure of energy. Whatever we might be able to say about the possibility of the evolution of life, certainly this would be impossible without the availability of highly energetic energy sources. Without employing such energy, the process comes to an immediate halt, and any products produced would suffer an inexorable thermal degradation. If such energy is introduced, however, the substances are destroyed at enormous rates, rates which far, far exceed the rates at which further steps up the evolutionary ladder can proceed. The evolution of life chemist is thus caught between the horns of a dilemma—with energy he's dead, without energy he's dead.

Energy Needed In Molecular Origins

The same processes and principles discussed above apply to all compounds that would have been required for the origin of life—not only amino acids and sugars, but also purines, pyrimidines, organic acids and amines, lipids, vitamins, etc. Why pursue the matter further? It is certain that if the production in significant quantities of these relatively simple organic compounds under any plausible hypothetical primitive earth conditions can be excluded, the production of more complex substances under these conditions is obviously impossible, and a mechanistic, naturalistic origin of life is therefore precluded. Nevertheless, let us pursue the problem further.

Amino acids have two reactive chemical groups—an amino group and a carboxyl group. The amino group of one amino acid may combine with the carboxyl group of another amino acid as water is split out and a chemical bond is formed between the amino group of one amino acid and the carboxyl group of the other:

$$
\underbrace{
\begin{array}{cc}
R & O \\
| & \| \\
H_2NCH-COH
\end{array}
}_{\substack{\text{carboxyl} \\ \text{group}}}
\quad + \quad
\underbrace{
\begin{array}{cc}
R & O \\
| & \| \\
HN-CHCOH \\
| \\
H
\end{array}
}_{\substack{\text{amino} \\ \text{group}}}
\longrightarrow
$$

$$
\begin{array}{cccc}
R & O & R & O \\
| & \| & | & \| \\
H_2NCHC & - & NCHCOH & + H_2O \\
& & | & \\
& & H &
\end{array}
$$

The product, called a dipeptide, has a free amino group that can combine with the carboxyl group of another amino acid and a free carboxyl group that can combine with the amino group of another amino acid. In this way the chain can be extended indefinitely. The average protein in living cells today is made up of about 400 amino acids of 20 different kinds, although a very few are small (insulin has 55 amino acids), and some are very large, with up to several thousand amino acids.

The formation of the chemical bond between the two amino acids (or amino acid residues that remain after water is split out)—called a peptide bond—requires energy. On the average, the formation of this chemical bond requires the expenditure of about 2.75 kilocalories per mole. On the other hand, the splitting of the bond, called hydrolysis since the elements of water are added, releases 2.75 k-cal per mole.

The thermodynamic barrier to a natural, spontaneous formation of a protein becomes immediately obvious. Consider, for example, the thermodynamics involved in the formation of a protein of 100 amino acids. This would constitute a protein of very modest size. To form a protein of 100 amino acids would require the synthesis of 99 peptide bonds. The synthesis of each one of these bonds would require about 2.75 k-cal per mole. Thus, none of these bonds would form spontaneously. Some means would have to be provided to feed in the required energy through an appropriate mechanism.

Since rupture of each one of these peptide bonds releases energy, however, rupture (hydrolysis) of these bonds does occur spontaneously. Thus, to form the protein, 99 peptide bonds must form, none of which want to form, none of which will form spontaneously, each bond formation requiring the expenditure of 2.75 k-cal of energy. To destroy this protein, however, only *one* bond anywhere in the molecule need rupture, and *that* does happen naturally and spontaneously, releasing 2.75 k-cal per mole.

Now none of us would be surprised to see a pingpong ball bouncing down a series of steps. In fact all of us have seen that happen at one time or an^ther. We would all be astounded, however, to see a ping pong ball spontaneously bouncing up a set of stairs. In fact, in all of our experience we have never seen that happen, nor do we ever expect to see it happen.

The same would be true for the spontaneous formation of a protein, although this would not be as obvious to most people as the example of the pingpong ball. A few calculations may help, however, An equilibrium constant corresponding to a $\triangle$ F of + 2.75 k-cl/mole is approximately 0.01. This means, starting with amino acids, that one per cent would spontaneously combine to form a dipeptide, 0.01% would end up in the form of a tripeptide, 0.0001% as a tetrapeptide, and the probability of forming a decapeptide (a polypeptide of 10 amino acids) would be only 10^{-20} (if the process were occurring in an aqueous medium, such as the ocean, the equilibrium would be shifted back towards free amino acids, and the probability would be far less). The probability of the spontaneous formation of a protein of any kind as large as insulin, a proten of only 55 amino acids, one of the smallest proteins known, would be 10^{-110}, a probability that can be equated to zero.

Furthermore, it must be understood that when we are talking about probability relationships here, we are referring only to thermodynamic considerations—the probability of forming a protein with amino acids arranged in *any* sequence. If we include probability considerations based on getting the correct sequence of amino acids to give specifically the insulin molecule, then of course the probability of the spontaneous formation of this molecule would be reduced much further yet.

We have established beyond doubt, based on thermodynamic considerations alone, that it is impossible for a protein to form spontaneously. In fact, Blum admits that "The spontaneous formation of a polypeptide of the size for the smallest known proteins seems beyond all probability."[14] This means, then, that a driving mechanism of some kind must be provided to *force* the amino acids to combine while at the same time stabilizing the molecule against rupture of the many relatively labile bonds it contains. This would, indeed, require some very special mechanism.

A living cell, of course, is provided with such a special mechanism. Dozens of enzymes are involved, certain complex organized elements in the cell participate, energy in specialized forms is delivered to the right place at the right time, etc. In fact, practically everything in the cell participates in protein synthesis. Organic chemists can synthesize proteins, too, of course, but in spite of all their ingenuity, specialized reagents, carefully chosen solvents, careful temperature control, and complex equipment, it takes them months to do a very poor job, relatively speaking, what the cell can do perfectly in seconds. Both living cells and organic chemists can, then, synthesize proteins in spite of thermodynamic problems. They do so, however, only because they provide a complex driving mechanism that overcomes this thermodynamic problem.

DNA and RNA Formation

The problems involved in the formation of DNA and RNA molecules would be even worse than those involved in protein synthesis. The subunits of DNA and RNA are nucleotides. Each nucleotide consists of a purine or pyrimidine, a five-carbon sugar (ribose for RNA and deoxyribose for DNA), and phosphoric acid. A DNA or RNA molecule may consist of hundreds and usually thousands of nucleotides.

A DNA or RNA Molecule of 1000 nucleotides would require the formation of 3000 chemical bonds (one for each of the purine or pyrimidine, sugar, and phosphoric acid in the chain). Thus, the formation of such a polynucleotide would require the formation of 3000 chemical bonds, none of which want to form, each of which would require the expenditure of energy. On the other hand, destruction of this molecule would require the rupture of only one of the three thousand chemical bonds involved in its formation, and *that* wants to happen.

Now let us go back to the hypothetical primordial earth with a scenario that includes an ocean that somehow, in spite of the thermodynamic impossibility, is populated with amino acids, sugars, purines, pyrimidines, phosphoric acid, etc. Lightning flashes in the atmosphere, and the full spectrum of the sun's radiation penetrates to the surface of the earth. Where in this scenario does one find the

77

mechanism for overcoming the overwhelming thermodynamic forces that dictate that no protein, no DNA or RNA or complex molecule of any kind could ever form spontaneously, even if one could imagine a primordial ocean rich in the required sub-units? What was there to accomplish this incredible task?

Was it time? Some have insisted that time is the hero of the plot. What seems impossible in the short view becomes inevitable if sufficient time is available, we are told. No, that is faulty reasoning. If everything tends to go from order to disorder, from complex to simple, if the random state is the more probable state, then the more time available the more probable it is that a system will be in its more probable state, that is, in a state of greater randomness and disorder.

Could it be the powerful stream of energy flowing to the earth from the sun? This is the answer to the problem that is suggested by practically every evolutionist who makes any kind of suggestion at all. The earth is not an isolated system: it is open to the radiant energy from the sun. It is this energy, we are told, that overcomes the thermodynamic barrier between simple substances and their combination to form complex compounds. This energy is the mechanism that solves all thermodynamic problems, including the problem posed by the second law, we are told.

We have already seen, however, that this energy cannot be the answer. It's efficacy as a destructive agent is far more effective than its efficacy as a constructive agent. If this raw, uncontrolled energy destroys even the simple molecule of glycine at a rate that exceeds by a million-fold the rate at which it is effective in forming glycine, how can it be used to form much, much more complex compounds, such as proteins and DNA? Ultraviolet light is used to sterilize substances precisely because it does very rapidly and efficiently destroys proteins, DNA and RNA.

Oxygen-Ozone Problem

If the layer of ozone that surrounds the earth were removed, allowing all the radiant energy from the sun to reach the surface of the earth, all life, from microorganisms to man, would rapidly be snuffed out. This is because the shortwave, highly energetic, highly destructive portion of the radiant energy from the sun is absorbed by ozone. The removal of this protective shield of ozone would allow this deadly energy to reach the earth and destroy all living things.

According to the evolutionary scenario that must be suggested by evolutionists, there could have been no protective shield of ozone in the hypothetical primordial atmosphere. Ozone is composed of triatomic oxygen. Ultraviolet light from the sun converts ordinary diatomic molecular oxygen into ozone. If there were no oxygen in the primordial atmosphere then there could have been no ozone. Evolutionists must, of necessity, exclude oxygen from their primitive earth scenario, however. If oxygen were present, all organic substances, such as amino acids, sugars, etc. would be oxidized to carbon dioxide, water, and other oxidized substances.

Oxygen is thus incompatible with an evolutionary scenario, but then so is its absence! No oxygen, no ozone. No ozone, no protection from the deadly destructive short wave ultraviolet light that is rapidly fatal for the existence of amino acids, proteins, DNA, and RNA. Again, the evolutionist is caught between the horns of a dilemma.

Blum is acutely aware of the thermodynamic problems that would be involved in attempting to imagine a naturalistic evolutionary origin of life. After mentioning the vital necessity of protein enzymes, Blum states *"The riddle seems to be: How, when no life existed, did substances come into being which today are absolutely essential to living system yet which can only be formed by those systems?"*[15] (emphasis in the original). The catalytic activity of enzymes would be absolutely essential to any system on its way to becoming life, yet they can be synthesized only by living things.

In the pages following Blum's statement cited above, he stresses the requirement for a mechanism for harnessing the energy of the sun. He states, "However, we regard the problem, we must admit that photosynthesis of some kind, perhaps very different from any we know today, arose very early in the course of organic evolution, if *indeed it was not involved from the beginning"*[16] (emphasis added). Certainly some form of energy mobilization had to be present from the very beginning, not only at the beginning of organic evolution but of chemical evolution itself.

We must emphasize in the strongest terms possible that merely bathing the earth in the radiant energy from the sun does *not* provide an energy mobilizing mechanism. As noted earlier, running a chemical reaction uphill is a tricky business. Merely pouring energy into a mixture of chemicals will not suffice to convert simple chemicals into complex chemicals when a significant thermodynamic barrier or series of barriers stand in the way. Special mechanisms must be available for trapping the incoming energy and converting it into a form that can be utilized by the system, and kinetic barriers must exist in the system to prevent premature release of the energy.

Photosynthesis

Today such a system exists in green plants and in photosynthetic organisms. Photosynthesis involves two photosystems, in each of which electrons are raised to an excited state and transported in such a way that this energy can be utilized within the system (Figure 1):

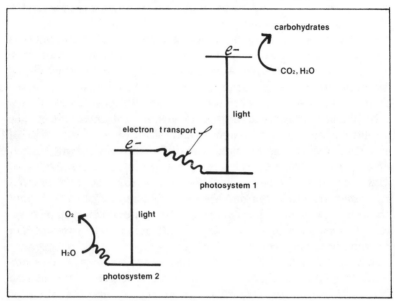

Figure 1 The mechanism of photosynthesis

Photosynthesis is, of course, a very complicated process involving many complex substances. It also involves the visible portion of the solar spectrum that penetrates the atmosphere, including the ozone shield. Living things thus are provided with a marvelous mechanism for harnessing the radiant energy of the sun, including an ozone shield for absorbing the destructive short wave ultraviolet light from the sun, and a complex system for converting the visible light that penetrates this shield into chemical energy that can be utilized by these forms of life. *Only because of this mechanism* is it possible for systems here on the earth to utilize the energy from the sun to convert simple chemicals, such as carbon dioxide, water, ammonia, and phosphorous, into complicated chemicals such as proteins and DNA. The fact that the earth is an open system bathed in radiant energy from the sun is a necessary *but not sufficient* condition for overcoming the thermodynamic barrier to the origin of complex chemicals and complex systems on the earth. A complex photosynthetic mechanism must exist to utilize that energy, but the origin of that mechanism is precisely what the origin of life chemist must explain in the first place! Babies aren't difficult to account for if you start with parents, but accounting for the first parents poses a more difficult problem.

Evolutionary Attempts

Sidney Fox has gained considerable attention for his so-called thermal scenario for the synthesis of proteins. His scheme has been severely criticized elsewhere,[17] and can be dismissed at best as a mere exercise in organic chemistry and at worst as pseudoscience not worthy of discussion.

Some have assumed that somehow Ilya Prigogine has solved the problem of the origin of biological order and the second law. Prigogine is the Belgian scientist who won the Nobel prize for his work relating non-equilibrium thermodynamics to the function of living things. Prigogine certainly has *not* solved the problem of the origin of biological order and the second law, and in fact he makes no such claims. he says, "There seems to be no doubt that dissipative structures play an essential role in the function of living systems as we see them today. What was the role of dissipative structures in evolution? It is very tempting to speculate that prebiotic evolution corresponds essentially to a succession of instabilities leading to an increasing level of complexity."[18] A temptation to speculate is, of course, not necessarily a solution to the problem!

Prigogine's speculative model is enshrouded with a considerable amount of complex mathematics that is difficult if not impossible to understand by non-mathematicians. This immediately renders it incomprehensible to most scientists, certainly to most biologists. Nevertheless, Prigogine's model sounds deliciously scientific and it has been eagerly welcomed by evolutionists who are looking for a way to overcome the insuperable barrier the second law of thermodynamics poses against an evolutionary origin of life. When Prigogine moves his mathematical model off of paper and out into the real world, however, it then becomes possible for a non-mathematician to examine the chemical and biological assumptions which serve as the basis of his model. An examination of these assumptions reveals that they are totally devoid of any foundation. His model offers no solution whatsoever.

In Prigogine's "evolution model,"[19] a system open to the flow of two monomer species a and b (which may correspond to two kinds of nucleotides, for example, adenylic acid and thymidylic acid) is assumed. Although he doesn't say much about it, a steady in-flow of energy in the form of energy-rich organic chemical molecules must also somehow be provided, and a way must exist to link this in-flow of energy to the synthetic process assumed in the model. Right at this preliminary stage, even before the more serious difficulties of his model are encountered, the model loses all plausibility.

In the absence of living organisms, it would be impossible to supply a sufficient quantity of either the nucleotides or the energy-rich organic molecules to provide the required concentration of these molecules, as we have already discussed.

Even if the ocean were swarming with these molecules, however, Prigogine's model could not explain how life could have evolved. From monomer a, which for the purpose of illustration Prigogine takes to be the nucleotide, adenylic acid (A), Prigogine assumes that the homopolymer, poly-adenylic acid (poly-A) is formed. Poly-A codes for (provides the template for) poly-thymidylic acid (poly-T), so in the presence of poly-A and a supply of thymidylic acid, Prigogine assumes that poly-T will form. Since poly-A not only codes for poly-T, but poly-T codes for poly-A, Prigogine asserts that when this stage is reached, an autocatalytic cycle is switched on. Let us pause here to examine assumptions made at this stage of the model.

First of all, Prigogine assumes that the monomers (the nucleotides) will combine to form polymers in huge quantities (many billions of tons of each polymer must form in order to produce a significant concentration in an ocean containing 350 million cubic miles of water). We have already discussed why no significant quantity of polymers such as protein and DNA could never form under any plausible primitive earth conditions.

Secondly, even if formation of polymer occurred at a significant rate to produce a significant overall amount of polymer, with two monomers present, such as adenylic acid (A) and thymidylic acid (T), it would still be impossible for a significant amount of a particular polymer to form. How in the world would formation of polymers be restricted to poly-A (A-A-A-A-A-A-A-A-A-----A) and poly-T (T-T-T-T-T-T-T-T------T)? Every possible sequence of A and T would form. For example, the polymer T-A-A-T-A-T-T-T-A-T-A-A-A-T-T, or any other sequence of A and T, would be just as likely to form as a polymer containing 15 A's or 15 T's exclusively. If polymers of 100 nucleotides were formed under assumed primitive earth conditions from only two monomers, 2^{100} (10^{30}, or a million billion billion) different combinations would be produced. This would completely eliminate the possibility of producing a significant quantity of any one particular polymer.

Thirdly, to claim that the presence of two polymers, such as poly-A and poly-T, would establish an autocatalytic cycle is sheer nonsense. Such a system could not be autocatalytic, since neither poly-A nor poly-T (or any other polynucleotide) is catalytic. Neither has the ability to speed up any chemical reaction, in this case the rate at which the bonds linking the nucleotides are formed. Thus neither can be called a catalyst. Prigogine nevertheless calls the assumed cycle autocatalytic, since poly-A codes (provides a template) for poly-T, which in turn codes for poly-A. Thus, he asserts, the rate of production of poly-A would at least be proportional to its concentration. But what Prigogine neglects to mention is that *the rate of destruction of poly-A (or poly-T) would also, be proportional to its concentration.* Since both the rate of production and the rate of destruction would tend to increase as the concentration tended to increase, no net effect on the overall concentration would result.

But now, going on with further assumptions in Prigogine's model (in spite of the impossibilities encountered so far), Prigogine assumes that in the formation of poly-A under the coding action of poly-T, errors occur, and as a result a new polymer is formed (let us call it polymer-X). Polymer-X, Prigogine assumes, may now direct the synthesis of a new substance E. He further assumes that E might possibly be a "primitive" protein enzyme which catalyzes the production of polymer-X, as well as its own production. The appearance of this catalyst, it is assumed, produces polymer-X at a much more rapid rate than either poly-A or poly-T is being produced, so the system rapidly shifts far from equilibrium until a new equilibrium is established. Now let us pause once again to see what is wrong with Prigogine's assumptions.

Firstly, no polynucleotide can direct the synthesis of a protein. All enzymes are proteins, and consist of long chains of amino acids. In living organisms the gene (a polynucleotide consisting of deoxyribonucleic acid or DNA) for each protein provides only the code for the sequence in which the amino acids occur in the protein, *and that is all it does.* The translation of this information, and the actual synthesis of the protein, requires much, much more.

DNA is only one of many different kinds of molecules required for the synthesis of a protein. To assert that a DNA molecule could direct the synthesis of a protein in the absence of the entire complex apparatus required for this task is simply absurd.

Furthermore, to say that the process was much simpler in the first step toward a living thing is totally contradicted by the evidence. For example, amino acids cannot align themselves along either a DNA or an RNA molecule. There is no "lock-and-key" fit, or any other kind of fit, between any amino acid and any nucleotide. It is chemically and physically impossible, for this reason alone, then, for a DNA or RNA molecule to "direct" the synthesis of a protein. In fact, the chemistry that would naturally occur would wreak havoc on any evolving life.

Secondly, no enzyme is capable of catalyzing both the synthesis of a polynucleotide, such as DNA or RNA, and itself. Thus, there is no enzyme known that catalyzes the formation of chemical bonds between nucleotides to form polynucleotides, and which also catalyzes the formation of chemical bonds between amino acids to form proteins. The chemistry involved in the formation of inter-nucleotide bonds is just too different from the chemistry involved in the formation of chemical bonds between amino acids for that to be possible.

Thirdly, as mentioned above, Prigogine assumes that the "primitive enzyme" catalyzes the production of polymer-X, which codes for his "primitive enzyme." The action of any enzyme cannot be restricted to the formation of any particular polynucleotide, however. There are DNA-polymerases in a cell which catalyze the formation of all DNA molecules. Thus, if Prigogine's hypothetical primitive enzyme did arise, it would not only catalyze the formation of polymer-X, but it would also catalyze the formation of every other polynucleotide that could possibly exist. Thus it would catalyze the formation of the original polymers, poly-A and poly-T, just as readily as it would catalyze the formation of polymer-X. Polymer-X, since it arose originally in a very small amount by error, would remain in very small quantity, relative to the original polymers.

Fourthly, the possibility that just by chance an error in the synthesis of poly-A would produce a new polymer (polymer-X) that is capable of directing the synthesis of a primitive enzyme defies the laws of probability, even if a polynucleotide could indeed direct the synthesis of a protein. No one knows just how an enzyme is capable of catalyzing a particular chemical reaction, but we do know that for the catalysis of a particular chemical reaction only one, or a very few, of the almost infinite possible arrangements of the amino acids in the protein enzyme will work. Each particular chemical task establishes rigid limits on what particular molecules can act as catalysts.

Most present day enzymes consist of protein molecules containing several hundred amino acids (there are 20 different kinds of amino acids in these proteins). Thus, even a "primitive" enzyme would probably require at least a hundred amino acids. No one really knows, of course, for we have no "primitive" enzymes to study today. Usually the removal of just a few amino acids from either end of present-day enzymes completely destroys their activity, leaving nothing that possesses "primitive" enzyme activity. If we assume, however, that the "primitive" enzyme consists of 100 of the 20 different amino acids that now exist in proteins and that a hundred billion (10^{11}) different possible arrangements of these 100 amino acids, rather than only one or a very few, precise arrangements (as is true in present day living things) might be able to function as the primitive enzyme, the possiblity by chance of getting even a single molecule, let alone billions of tons, of any one of these hundred billion primitive enzymes would essentially be nil.

One hundred amino acids of 20 different kinds can be arranged in 20^{100} (10^{130}) different ways. If 10^{11} of these could function as the primitive enzyme, and if a billion trillion (10^{21}) of the various protein molecules of 100 amino acids formed each second for five billion years (approximately 10^{17} seconds) the chance of getting a single molecule of one of the required sequences is 10^{21} x 10^{17} x 10^{11} / 10^{130}, or only one chance out of 10^{81}. This probability is for all practical purposes a nil probability.

Summarizing, in Prigogine's model he assumes:

1. A steady net production of enormous quantities of nucleotides and amino acids on the hypothetical primitive earth by the simple interaction of raw energy and simple gases.
2. A steady net production of enormous quantities of energy-rich organic molecules to supply the required energy.
3. The combination, in enormous quantities, of the nucleotides to form polymers (DNA).
4. The selective formation of homopolymers (such as poly-A and poly-T) rather than the formation of mixed polymers of random sequences.
5. The establishment of an autocatalytic cycle.
6. Errors in the formation of the polymers producing a new polymer which directs the synthesis of a primitive protein enzyme.
7. The primitive protein enzyme catalyzes the formation of both itself and the nucleotide polymer (DNA).
8. The above molecules somehow manage to spontaneously separate themselves from the rest of the world and concentrate into condensed systems coordinated in time and in space.

Not a single one of the above assumptions has any shred of probability under any plausible primitive earth conditions. Improbability piled on improbability equals impossibility.

A mathematical model of almost any imagined process can be made to work on paper as certain assumptions are made. When the model is moved off the paper and out into the real world of chemistry and physics and the assumptions of the model are translated into processes which can actually be tested, it then becomes possible to determine whether the model has any validity. As can be seen from the above discussion, Prigogine's model has no validity whatsoever.

Of course, the basic assumption overshadowing all of Prigogine's speculative model is easily challenged. This is his assumption that a sudden movement of a system to a state far from equilibrium might stabilize the system in a new, more complex state. Neither Prigogine nor anyone else has been able to suggest a single example in the world of chemistry to support such an idea. Certainly a movement far from equilibrium (that which preceeds an explosion, for example) may easily lead to greater randomness, but it is difficult to visualize how such processes might generate complexity.

Since the tendency in every part of the universe at every level of organization is to go in the direction of increasing disorder, any movement away from equilibrium would tend to accelerate the movement toward greater disorder or randomness. Even if it were possible by some as yet unknown mechanism to generate on rare occasions a more complex system, the next perturbation in the system would move it back in the direction of less complexity and greater disorder. An increase in complexity does not increase stability. The more complex an organic chemical molecule is, the less stable it is and the greater the tendency to undergo degradation. Thus, proteins are much less stable than their constituent amino acids and DNA is much less stable than the purines and pyrimidines which are constituents of the building blocks which make up DNA. Prigogine's model can be rejected on the basis of common experience in the real world of chemistry and for total lack of support based on actual empirical evidence.

Manfred Eigen and his theories on increasing biological order by means of epicycles involving autocatalytic molecules[20] can be rejected on the basis of two vitally important facts. First, his system begins with complex organic chemical molecules. It is the very origin of such compounds that evolutionists must explain. Secondly, there is no such thing as an autocatalytic molecule. Biochemists have as yet failed to discover a single molecule in either the living or non-living world that catalyzes its own formation. Eigen's model, like that of Prigogine, is one that looks appealing on paper but when moved off of paper and out into the real world of chemistry, simply does not and cannot work.

Crystallization and Origins

Finally, a few words should be said about crystallization and the origin of biological order. Crystallization is frequently cited as proof that the second law of thermodynamics cannot be used as evidence against evolution. It is claimed that crystallization (including the formation of snowflakes) is an increase in order that obviously occurs spontaneously, and therefore the second law does not prevent the spontaneous increase in order in an open system where heat (and thus energy) can be exchanged with the surroundings.

First let it be pointed out that crystallization is completely irrelevant to the question of evolution. Crystallization is a totally different process than evolution. In crystallization, matter is arranging itself in a *lower* energy state and therefore in a *more probable* state. In fact, a crystal is at equilibrium. No processes occur in the crystal. It is an inert system. In origin of life schemes, on the other hand, matter is arranging itself into a state of *higher* energy content and therefore in a *less probable* state. Every step in the origin of life would be an uphill struggle. The free energy content, and therefore the instability, the tendency to spontaneously degrade, increases with each step upward. Crystallization and the origin of life process are thus two diametrically opposed processes.

Mora states "Crystallization occurs because it leads to the lowest energy state, and to the most stable arrangement of atoms or molecules under the given conditions. Crystallization leads to simple, very uniform repeating structures, which are inert. These structures do not function, and are not designed by function."[21]

Stravropoulos, in discussing a suggestion of Weisskopf[22] concerning the possibility of a "fourth law of thermodynamics" as an explanation of the origin of biological order, states "I must disagree with Dr. Weisskopf's discussion of the effects of the second law of thermodynamics on order-disorder phenomena and the 'hierarchies' of nature for the following reasons:

"He makes it appear as though crystals and highly ordered organic molecules belong to the same class, when in fact they do not. When a crystal is broken up, the smaller crystals are physically and chemically identical to the original. This is never observed with (organic) molecules; when the original molecule is split up lesser molecules appear, and part of the original information is lost. To ignore such fundamental differences in an effort to arrive at some general overview or law is to create a false overview, a pseudo law."[23]

Yockey states, "Attempts to relate the idea of 'order' in a crystal with biological organization or specificity must be regarded as a play on words which cannot stand careful scrutiny."[24]

Prigogine, Nicolis, and Babloyantz say "The point is that in a nonisolated system there exists a possibility for formation of ordered, low-entropy structures at sufficiently low temperatures. This ordering principle is responsible for the appearance of ordered structures such as crystals as well as for the phenomena of phase transitions.

"Unfortunately this principle cannot explain the formation of biological structures. The probability that at ordinary temperatures a macroscopic number of molecules is assembled to give rise to the highly ordered structures and to the coordinated functions characterizing living organisms is vanishingly small."[25]

Mora, Stravropoulos, Yockey, and Prigogine all emphasize that the "order" in a crystal is of an entirely different nature than the order found in organic molecules and the organized systems found in living things. To use the example of crystallization as proof that thermodynamics, and specifically the second law, cannot be used against evolution is based on sheer ignorance of the fundamental differences between these two processes.

Chemical Natural Selection

Sometimes evolutionists attempt to rescue themselves from the seemingly hopeless morass that encompasses the origin of life scenario by invoking some form of natural selection in the chemical world. Whatever else can or cannot be said about natural selection as an effective mechanism for explaining evolution in the living world, it certanly cannot be invoked in the non-living world. Natural selection is nothing more than differential reproduction, and of course reproduction occurs only in the living world. No organic molecule reproduces itself. Not even viruses are capable of reproduction. Viruses are replicated only by living cells.

Almost all scientists recognize that natural selection cannot be used as a mechanism for the origin of life. Blum says, for example, "The present composition of living systems is the ultimate result of their past history, extending back to the moment of their origin from non-living material itself. Before that time mutation and natural selection could not exist, since they depend upon properties which are characteristic of living systems only, so the derivation of the basic materials must have involved other factors."[26]

With this fact in mind it is interesting to consider some figures suggested by Julian Huxley for the evolution of a complex creature, such as a horse, from a single-celled organism *without* natural selection.[27] Without going into detail here, we wish to point out that Huxley, even though several of his assumptions were acknowledged as being generous towards the evolutionary side, calculated that the odds against getting a horse from a single-celled organism by evolution through mutation without natural selection was $(1/1000)^{1,000,000}$. That is equal to one chance out of the number one followed by three million zeroes.

Huxley of course acknowledged that these were obviously impossible odds, but nevertheless it did happen—thanks to the workings of natural selection! It seems equally obvious that natural selection is the evolutionist's God, for surely no *natural* force or process could overcome odds of that kind.

Surely, however, the odds against the evolution of life would be much greater than odds against the evolution of the horse from a single cell without natural selection. The probability of matter existing in the form of a "simple" bacterial cell compared to its probability of existing in the form of the elements from which it is derived is $10^{-10^{11}}$, as we have noted earlier. Now if, as Huxley admits, the evolution of the horse from a single-celled organism without natural selection is unquestionably impossible, then beyond a shadow of a doubt the evolution of life is impossible because the odds against the evolutionary origin of life are much greater than the odds against getting the horse and it is impossible to appeal to natural selection in any origin of life schemes.

Conclusion

Everywhere in the observable universe, at every level, from the atom to the galaxies, scientists observe an all-pervasive unceasing tendency for matter to become more disordered, less complex. This tendency is so unfailing that it has been formalized as a natural law, the second law of thermodynamics.

The origin of life would have required an incredible increase in order and complexity involving many millions of local decreases in entropy, and mechanisms for accomplishing this plus stabilization of the structures derived, all of which supposedly occurred in spite of the natural tendency to go in the opposite direction.

The evolutionary scenario begins with a primitive earth surrounded by a primordial atmosphere of simple gases bombarded by the deadly destructive ultraviolet light of the sun and electrical discharges. Somewhere in all of this, according to evolutionists, exists a remarkable mechanism. This mechanism is so all-powerful, all-pervasive, so precisely effective and specifically directed that it is sufficient to conquer the all-pervasive unceasing tendency of matter to become disordered.

This mechanism would have to be so powerful, so all-pervasive that it would be obvious to all scientists, regardless of their philosophical persuasion. After a careful search of much of the literature on this subject, however, I have failed utterly to find it. Certainly a thorough search of the publications of Prigogine, Blum, Morowitz and others fails to uncover it. Suggestions have been many—crystallization, open systems with flow-through of energy, differential rates of movement toward disorder, irreversible thermodynamics with sudden movements far from equilibrium, epicycles with "autocatalytic" molecules. All fail close scrutiny. As far as scientists have been able to determine so far, no such mechanism exists. A consideration of all available scientific data, taking into account all established principles and natural laws, is coercively convincing that the second law of thermodynamics and all the data on which it is based renders a mechanistic, naturalistic evolutionary origin of life impossible,or as impossible as anything could be considered impossible in science.

REFERENCES

[1] Poter, V.R., 1970, *Perspectives in biology and medicine,* Autumn, p. 139.

[2] Oparin, A. I. 1957, The origin of life on the earth, Academic Press, New York, pp. 349-350.

[5] Green, D. F., and R. F. Goldberger, 1967, Molecular insights into the living process, Academic Press, New York, p. 407.

[4] Morowitz, H. J. 1968, Energy flow in biology, Academic Press, p. 7.

[5] Lindsay, R. B. 1968, *American Scientist,* 56(2):100.

[6] Blum, H. 1955, *American Scientist,* 43(4):595.

[7] Asimov, I. 1970, *Smithsonian Institution Journal,* June, p. 6.

[8] Simpson, G. G. and W. S. Beck, 1965, Life . . . an introduction to biology, Harcourt, brace, and World, New York, p. 466.

[9] Wrighton, M. S. 1979 *Chemical and Engineering News,* September 3, p. 31.

[10] Blum, H. 1968, Time's arrow and evolution, 3rd Ed., Princeton University Press, Princeton, p. 94.

[11] Hull, D. E., 1960, *Nature,* 186:693-694.

[12] Blum, H. 1968, *Op cit.* pp. 191-192.

[13] Miller, S. 1953, *Science,* 117:528-529.

[14] Blum, H. 1968, *Op cit.* p. 158.

[15] Blum, H. 1968, *Op cit.,* p. 164.

[16] Blum, H. 1968, *Op cit.* p. 166.

[17] Gish, D.T. 1979, *Creation Research Society. Quarterly* 15(4):185-203.

[18] Nicolis, G. and I Prigogine, 1977, Self-organization in nonequilibrium systems, John Wiley and Sons, New York, p. 1.

[19] Prigogine, I., G. Nicolis, and A. Babloyantz, 1972, *Physics Today,* 25(11):23-28.

[20] Eigen, M. and P. Schuster, The hypercycle, Springer-Verlag, New York, 1979.

[21] Mora, P. T. 1963, *Nature,* 199:216.

[22] Weisskopf, V. F. 1977, *American Scientist,* 65:409.

[23] Stravropoulos, G. P. 1977, *American Scientist,* 65:675.

[24] Yockey, H. P. 1977, *Journal of Theoretical Biology,* 67:380.

[25] Prigogine, I., G. Nicolis, and A. Babloyantz, 1972, *Op. cit.* p. 23.

[26] Blum, H. 1968, *Op cit.* p. 194.

[27] Huxley, J. 1953, Evolution in action, The New American Library, New York, pp. 45-46.

5

Resistance Of Living Organisms
To The Second Law of Thermodynamics

Emmett L. Williams

Introduction

Inorganic systems are known to obey the second law of thermodynamics and hence tend to reach a state of maximum entropy. Living organisms also tend to reach a state of maximum entropy, but at a relatively slower rate.

The "life principle," whatever it may be, appears to sustain great order (low entropy) in the organism so much longer than one would expect in an inanimate system that it has led some scientists to claim that the second law of thermodynamics does not apply to living organisms.[1] This is a serious charge. If this basic law of science is violated in the living realm of nature, why can it not be violated under proper conditions in the inanimate realm of nature?

There is no valid experimental evidence of a violation of the second law of thermodynamics in either animate or inanimate material. This places the evolutionist in the position of passively or actively denying the observable (second law) to believe the unobservable (macroevolution).

The purpose of this paper is to examine the methodology of the thermodynamics of irreversible processes and its relation to living organisms, to see if creation or evolution offers the best interpretative framework for what is known. From this paper it is hoped that the reader will see that living systems do not appear to violate the second law. Not enough scientific information is available to relate thermodynamic methods rigorously to living systems.

Classical Thermodynamics and Time

Living systems appear to be more successful in resisting degeneration than non-living systems. The obvious variable involved is time. The living system will eventually degenerate, but not as rapidly as non-living material.

In classical thermodynamics time is *not* a variable, and is never considered. Normally a system is investigated in one state, allowed to change to another state and investigated again. Typical independent variables are temperature, pressure, volume, concentration, and entropy. They are specified at the state of interest.

After a change has occurred the total entropy change (dS) can be determined. Never is the rate of entropy change $\left(\dfrac{dS}{dt}\right)$ considered. Systems are never investigated conceptually in a state of change, but between one definite state and another.

The concept of entropy has taken on many interpretations from the necessary wastage of heat[2] in heat engines to a measure of disorder from statistical considerations[3]. Entropy can be considered as a thermodynamic potential, the sign of which indicates the direction taken by a spontaneous process.

If dS > O the process occurs spontaneously, and if dS < O the process is not spontaneous, but is forced by some external source. For irreversible processed in isolated systems the sign of dS will always be positive (i.e. dS > O)[4]. Isolated systems are considered conceptually simply because *only spontaneous* changes can occur in them[5]. The conclusion from this is that the entropy of any thermodynamic system will always increase during a spontaneous change.

Once the process is completed the entropy difference (dS = S_2 − S_1) between the initial state (1) and final state (2) is calculated. The rate of entropy change $\dfrac{dS}{dt}$ is never known.

If one wishes to calculate $\dfrac{dS}{dt}$ there must be a "wedding" between thermodynamics and kinetics (study of rate processes) so the rate of change can be introduced. The science of thermodynamics of irreversible processes has developed from these considerations. Although this relatively new science offers promise, the best efforts of researchers have simply verified the results obtainable from classical thermodynamic techniques[6].

Living Systems and Classical Thermodynamic Methodology

Living systems can be investigated qualitatively using classical thermodynamic methods. The necessary procedure is to choose an initial and final state and to determine *qualitatively* an order vs. disorder relationship between the two. If we use biological systems that require a male-female reproduction, immediately after conception we have a cell or cells with all of the genetic information available to grow into a mature adult if the proper energy is provided. Energy includes mass as well as its other forms. This initial state is highly ordered.

Consider the organism sometime after physical death (Ecc. 3:20). The organisms has decayed into dust. This final state is an example of gross disorder. From the initial order to the final state of disorder the entropy of the organism has increased. (See Figure 1) Thus it can be seen that living systems are subject to the second law. In any living system, this analysis will be true.

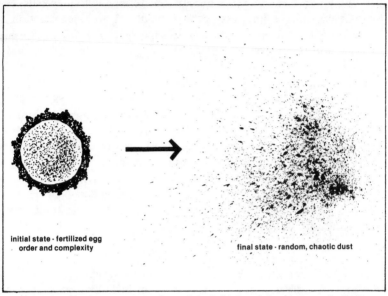

initial state · fertilized egg
order and complexity

final state · random, chaotic dust

Figure 1 Qualitative representation of the initial and final states of a living organism

Any living organism survives because it takes energy in from its surroundings. These energy transfer operations are inefficient. This inefficiency could contribute to the organism "wearing out" and finally dying. If these processes were 100% efficient, the organism could maintain itself much more easily.

It is impossible to perform many realistic quantitative calculations on the thermodynamics of living systems because of the state of the art of biology and the present methodology of classical thermodynamics. One of the problems is that conceptually all systems in classical thermodynamics must be able to be completely reversible, i.e. be able to return to an initial state at the finish of a cyclic process.

Very little thought is necessary to realize that living systems are in no way reversible, but they may be *carefully* examined as systems in which irreversible processes occur. But one must be extremely cautious in doing this. Note this comment by Kestin[7]:

> The need for the stipulation that the initial state 1 can *always* be restored from state 2 which had previously been reached by an irreversible process is fundamental to the development of therm-

odynamics because only then is it possible to determine the properties of systems by measurements conducted prior to the performance of a process. Without the knowledge of properties, no process could be analyzed in quantitative terms. Not all systems encountered in nature possess this attribute. A notable exception is afforded by all living organisms. Superficially, living organisms perform an irreversible process during their life cycle, but in stating this we yield to the impulse of using the term "irreversible process" semantically, and not in its technical meaning appropriate in thermodynamics. For this reason, systems like biological ones cannot be analyzed in terms of the equations of thermodynamics because no earlier state of such a system can ever be restored from a later state. Loosely speaking, one can say that a thermodynamic system possesses no "memory" or "history." A given state of the system is always described by its properties as they are measured at that state, and not by the details of the process, which enabled the system to assume the state under consideration.

Bridgman[8] makes this interesting remark:
One may anticipate that the extension of the entropy concept to more complicated phenomena, perhaps including ultimately the biological phenomena of life, is coextensive with the discovery of macroscopic parameters adequate for the exhaustive description of these phenomena.
Are these parameters available in the methodology of non-equilibrium thermodynamics?

Methodology of Thermodynamics of Irreversible Processes
Irreversible thermodynamic methods are used to deal with the behavior of a system during the course of an irreversible process[9]. As mentioned earlier this is a combination of the sciences of thermodynamics and kinetics. However some new postulates must be introduced, and if the calculations made using these new postulates check with those made assuming reversible transformations and classical laws, the postulates are assumed to be correct[10-12].

In many cases the validity of the postulates are not known[13]. This requirement poses the restriction that any process investigated cannot at anytime be too far from an equilibrium state since this is where classical laws apply. Much should be known about the irreversible process so that no mistakes are made in formulating the proper equations of state.

The central concept in both irreversible and classical thermodynamics is entropy[14,15]. The science has been developed on the premise that entropy increases in any irreversible adiabatic process[16]. In other words

$$dS \geq \frac{dQ_{rev}}{T} = dS_{rev} \qquad (1)$$

where dS is the entropy change because of an irreversible change, dS_{rev} is the entropy change because of a reversible change, dQ_{rev} is the heat gained or lost in a reversible process, and T is the absolute temperature.

The expression is normally integrated between an initial and final state (the start and finish of the process). This definition of entropy[17] is valid for closed systems (exchange of energy with surroundings), but biological systems are considered open systems (exchange of energy and mass with surroundings)[18].

Since it is necessary to visualize the flow of mass into and out of an open system* the change in entropy (dS) is split into two parts,[19] dS_e and dS_i where dS_e is the change in entropy because of interactions between system and surroundings (externally induced) and dS_i is the change in entropy occurring because of changes within the system (internally induced). Then,

$$dS = dS_e + dS_i \qquad (2)$$

and $dS_i > O$ for irreversible processes. $\qquad (3)$

Since it is desired to find the entropy change *during* a process, how can $\left(\dfrac{dS}{dt} \right)$ the entropy change with time, be visualized conceptually? Entropy is treated as a nonconserved fluid and the equation of continuity from fluid mechanics is used[20,21].

The key to a successful manipulation of the entropy property, is the artifice of visualizing entropy as a substance capable of flowing like water from one part of space to another[22].

Since entropy is an artificial construct, entropy flow cannot be measured directly (if such flow exists), whereas liquid flow (water, etc.) can be measured by a flowmeter. However there is no such device as an entropy flowmeter. This happens to be one of the weaknesses of the model. Using such a model a scientist can never be sure his calculations are correct unless he checks them against known results.

Normally the only way to check the calculated results is to compare them with known classical thermodynamic and kinetic evidences. If the calculations cannot be verified by direct observation, experimentation, or firmly established classical laws, then they are merely hypotheses.

°Obviously mass is a form of energy. Possibly in the future scientists will develop parameters so that energy in any form can be represented quite generally in thermodynamic equations of state.

There is certainly nothing wrong with this procedure. However, no great weight should be placed on unverifiable equations.

Pushing this objection aside, the model will be further developed. The entropy flux density ($\mathbf{J}_s$) is defined as the direction and magnitude of the entropy crossing a unit area perpendicular to the flow per unit time. (See Figure 2). Thus.

$$\mathbf{J}_s = \frac{dS}{dt} \frac{\mathbf{n}}{dA} \tag{4}$$

where $\mathbf{n}$ is unit vector perpendicular to dA the unit area and dA = dzdy. Equation 4 can be better represented as a scalar quantity.

$$\frac{dS}{dt} = \int \mathbf{n} \cdot \mathbf{J}_s dA \tag{5}$$

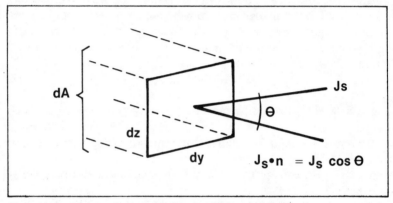

Figure 2 Representation of entropy flux ($\mathbf{J}_s$) through a unit area (dA = dydz)

$\dfrac{dS}{dt}$ is sometimes called the rate of entropy production, or the amount of

entropy created per unit time in an irreversible process. The amount of entropy leaving a unit volume per unit time is the excess of entropy that leaves the unit volume minus the entropy that enters the volume and can be represented using the divergence of a vector field[23].

$$\text{div } \mathbf{J}_s = \nabla \cdot \mathbf{J}_s = \frac{\partial J_{sx}}{\partial x} + \frac{\partial J_{sy}}{\partial y} + \frac{\partial J_{sz}}{\partial z} \tag{6}$$

Using the divergence theorem[24] the rate of entropy production for a volume (V) becomes

$$\int_A \mathbf{n} \cdot \mathbf{J}_s dA = \int_V \text{div } \mathbf{J}_s dV \tag{7}$$

Then for any volume (V) the rate of increase of entropy inside dV plus the outward flux of entropy from dV equals the entropy production inside dV. Mathematically this is represented as

$$\frac{\partial(\varrho s)}{\partial t} \, dV + (\text{div } \mathbf{J}_s) \, dV = \sigma dV \tag{8}$$

where ϱ is the density of the matter in dV and s is the entropy per unit mass such that $S = \int_V \varrho s dV$. σ is used to denote the rate of entropy production per unit volume $\dfrac{dS}{dt dV}$ Cancelling out dV,

$$\frac{\partial(\varrho s)}{\partial t} + \text{div } \mathbf{J}_s = \sigma. \tag{9}$$

This can be called the equation of continuity for entropy flow. For reversible processes[25]

$$\sigma = 0 \tag{10}$$

For irreversible processes

$$\sigma > 0 \tag{11}$$

Actually the quantities $\mathbf{J}_s$ and σ in Equation 9 are undefined[26]. Other postulates must be introduced so that a *choice* can be made for $\mathbf{J}_s$ and σ. Remember that a scientist's presuppositions will primarily determine what choice will be made. As yet there is no clear-cut way to find out $\mathbf{J}_s$ or σ, so that there is no direct verification for any chosen quantity unless it can be shown to agree with experimental results.

The mathematical sign (+ or −) of certain quantities is known from classical thermodynamics. Equations 3 and 11 are positive because entropy increases with irreversible changes that occur inside the system. Using these as guidelines some calculations yield verifiable results.[27] This is done by introducing empirical flow equations that depend upon gradients, such as heat flow which develops because of a change in temperature with distance. Examples of some gradient equations are given below:[28]

Heat Flow:
$$\mathbf{J}_H = -K_T \text{ grad } T \text{ (Fourier's law)} \tag{12}$$
Electric Current:
$$\mathbf{J}_E = -K \text{ grad } V \text{ (Ohm's law)} \tag{13}$$
Fluid Flow:
$$\mathbf{J}_F = -C_F \text{ grad } P \text{ (Poiseuille's law)} \tag{14}$$
Diffusion:
$$\mathbf{J}_D = -D \text{ grad } C \text{ (Fick's law)} \tag{15}$$

K_T is the thermal conductivity, K is the electrical conductivity, C_F is a frictional coefficient related to the viscosity, and D is the diffusion coefficient. T is temperature, V is electrical potential, P is pressure, and C is concentration. Yourgrau et al[29] state what has been accomplished utilizing this methodology:

> We should emphasize that this step represents a marriage between a purely thermodynamic result and a set of equations not derivable from thermodynamic principles. Admittedly the adoption of the recommended procedure has so far led only to relatively trivial results. This is attributable to the fact that we have ignored the possibility of one process affecting or interfering with another when they happen simultaneously.

Generalized flow equations are introduced for each process occurring in the system to overcome the difficulty with competing processes. The form of these equations is

$$J = LX \qquad (16)$$

Where X is the gradient or affinity causing the flux (J) and L is a constant. X is sometimes referred to as the thermodynamic force or potential. This would make Equation 16 a thermodynamic equation of motion. For n competing processes the total flux J_i is

$$J_i = \sum_{j=1}^{n} L_{ij} X_j \ (i = 1, 2, \ldots, n) \qquad (17)$$

$$L_{ij} = \left(\frac{\partial J_i}{\partial X_j}\right) x_k \qquad k \neq j \qquad (18)$$

Higher order terms are ignored. From this the entropy production σ is given as

$$\sigma = \sum_i J_i X_i \qquad (19)$$

or for several competing processes at once,

$$\sigma = \sum_i \sum_j L_{ij} X_i X_j \qquad (20)$$

The postulates for irreversible thermodynamics are as follows: **I.** The Gibbs equation for the first law is assumed to be true (even though the system is not at equilibrum).

$$dU = TdS - PdV + \sum_i \mu_i dw_i \qquad (21)$$

where dU is the change in internal energy of a system, TdS = dQ, the heat gained or lost by system, PdV is mechanical work done on or by steam (P is pressure and dV is volume change), μ_i is the partial specific Gibbs function of substance (i) (chemical or thermodynamic potential), and dw_i is the mass fraction of substance (i).

II. The rate of entropy production (σ) is the sum of the products of the forces and fluxes and is always greater than or equal to zero.

III. Each flux, to account for entropy production, is a linear combination of the forces (Equations 16 and 17). These postulates cannot be considered to be as rigorous as the first and second laws of thermodynamics and are not new principles equal to these two.[30]

Obtaining answers using the above equations is an arduous task (due to various system interactions). The Onsager reciprocity relations[31] are used to overcome many of the difficulties. The general form of the relations is shown below. They deal with the relationship between the gradients.

$$L_{ij} = L_{ji} \tag{22}$$

The relations are developed from atomic models and statistical assumptions on the behavior of these models.

The procedure used in determining the forces and fluxes, if not done properly, will completely invalidate the results[32]. As the theory becomes more advanced and more experimental work is accomplished, possible selection of forces and fluxes may become more scientific, but the reciprocity relations can never be considered universally valid, as are the first and second laws.[33]

Caution should be observed when working with the phenomenological equations so that a result contrary to the first and second laws is not obtained. The "tail should not wag the dog." The first and second laws must be given preeminence over kinetic considerations. Many evolutionists in their zeal to do away with the second law may choose to ignore this warning and allow kinetic considerations to override the second law regardless of the unscientific results of such a procedure. Tykodi[34] notes that

An obsessive concern with the explicit dependence of currents on affinities and other parameters of the system is rather uncharacteristic of thermodynamics: in the case of chemical equilibrium, for example, we do not need to know the exact kinetic mechanism (the precise forward and backward rate expressions) in order to find the thermodynamic conditions of equilibrium and the expression for the equilibrium constant. I feel that just as ordinary thermodynamics places its main emphasis on the conditions of equilibrium so the thermodynamics of steady states should place its *main* emphasis on the conditions of migrational equilibrium in given spatial fields rather than on problems of "matter and motion" (items that are more a part of general physics than of anything else). Furthermore, the fundamental experimental system is the container plus the contents plus the interaction of container and contents with the surroundings. The experimenter would prefer a global language that reflects the laboratory realities. Now the experimenter never *measures* directly what happens at a single point in space, and a language couched in terms of local properties and gradients makes his life that much more difficult and gives him little or no guidance in dealing with the effect on the container or the process being studied and in deciding on ways to minimize that effect.

Entropy Sinks Impossible

Many evolutionists try to justify their processes of development by making a claim that entropy could increase in one part of the universe while it is decreasing in this part of the universe as long as the total entropy content of the universe increases. This allows "evolution" to occur in a small part of the universe while the entropy of the total universe increases. Such a statement cannot be supported, and is an appeal to blind faith.

What the evolutionist is demanding is to have an entropy sink in a system. No part of any thermodynamic system, living or inanimate has ever been shown to act as an entropy sink. Essentially the claim is this:

$$dS_I \geq O \qquad (23)$$

I—An entropy increase in most of the universe. However,

$$dS_{II} \leq O \qquad (24)$$

II—An entropy decrease in the part of the universe where evolution has occurred. This would be justified as long as

$$dS_T = dS_I + dS_{II} \geq O \qquad (25)$$

where dS_T is the total entropy change in the system and $dS_I > dS_{II}$. However since evolution is an irreversible process[35], and $dS > O$ for irreversible process, then $dS_T = dS_I + dS_{II} \geq O$, but

$$dS_I \geq O \text{ and } dS_{II} \geq O \qquad (26)$$

since irreversible processes are occurring in both I and II and the first situation (equation 24) cannot be true[36].

Thus in one part of a system there can be no absorption of entropy (entropy sink) compensated by a sufficient production of entropy in another part of the system. Any irreversible process that occurs must cause an increase in entropy. In any living system there can be no entropy sink where entropy can be removed so that the organism can evolve. Eventually death will claim any living material and no rise in complexity and order can be expected from such a mechanism as this.

Living Systems as Steady States

In recent years a great deal of emphasis has been placed on mature or adult systems as being steady states[37-41]. It is imagined that as the living system grows to maturity or adulthood it changes from a non-steady to a steady state. The steady state is defined as a state that is time independent. Once a steady state is achieved it does not tend to change with time.

Obviously, no living system can exist forever as a time independent system. The model *completely* fails. Living systems are not steady states, since they die. Any attempt to avoid this by restricting the investigation to growth processes completely distorts the true picture of living organism.

Living organisms, in particular the human body, can be looked upon as constituting fuel cells. In a living organism the food intake serves as the fuel and the blood stream plays the art of the electrolye. The chemical reaction is enhanced by the catalytic action of enzymes, and as a result energy is produced by direct conversion from the chemical energy of the fuel-oxygen intake. A portion of this energy is electrical in nature. However, in contrast with man-made fuel cells, living organisms cannot operate in steady state over their life span, and cannot be regenerated; the irreversible changes which occur in them inevitably drive them to death[42].

Many times the wording of the thermodynamicist has been misunderstood by evolutionists. Consider this comment by Prigogine[43].

Further, the fact that during growth living organisms actually show a decrease of entropy production during evolution up to the stationary state.

Prigogine claims that dS/dt (rate of entropy production) decreases as an organism grows to maturity. It is not claimed that entropy decreases, only that the rate at which entropy increases is slower at maturity than during growth. The stationary or steady state is considered to be the state of minimum entropy production. This is very similar to equilibrium states in classical thermodynamics. The equilibrium state is the state of maximum entropy, and as the system approaches the equilibrium state its rate of increase of entropy becomes less and less until at equilibrium it reaches maximum disorder, and the entropy production rate is zero (no further increase in entropy possible), or the system approaches equilibrium asymptotically so that the rate of entropy increase is very slow as it nears equilibrium, as illustrated in Figure 3.

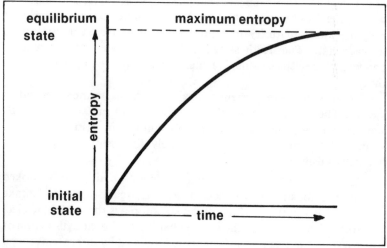

Figure 3 Asymptotic increase of entropy as system approaches equilibrium state

Evolution in this sense is simply limited change and not macroevolution from molecules to man. In other words as the living system grows (changes) to maturity (wrongly identified as the steady state) the rate of entropy production decreases. This is not a violation of the second law, and is similar to systems approaching the equilibrium state in classical thermodynamics.

Evolutionists err when they claim that the second law does not apply to living systems. In their zeal to claim an entropy decrease they fail to realize that it is the rate of entropy production that decreases, and *not* the entropy itself!

Many evolutionists erroneously conclude that during growth the organism is increasing in complexity and order. But growth should not be looked upon as a time of increase in order and complexity. Growth is definitely an increase in size, but the complexity and the genetic information necessary for growth was initially in the starting cell of the organism. The cell in no way "evolves" or acquires this order from any outside source. The capacity to attain maturity is in this starting state.

102

The starting cell must be more complex than any cell in the mature organism or at least equal in complexity.

Consider growth from a creationist standpoint. God created a fully-functioning universe and living organisms on earth. As far as can be determined from scripture the organisms were created fully grown. Using a classical thermodynamic qualitative approach the organisms simply fill the earth after its kind and replicate the original created order when adult produces adult, etc. (See Figure 4)

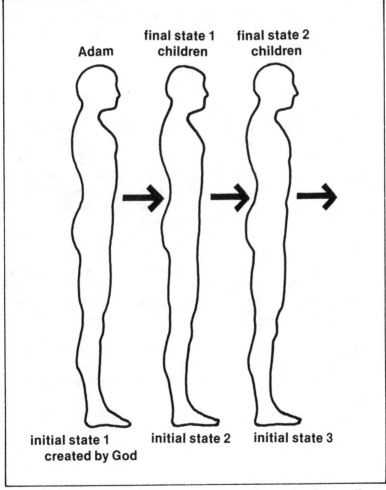

Figure 4 Schematic diagram of reproduction and growth of succeeding generations from initial created state

Adam had children which grew to maturity, they had children which grew to maturity, etc. From the initial to the final state there is no increase in order. Original order is at best being duplicated. When sin entered the world the disordering effects of the second law would have reduced the order in successive generations by mutations.

Thus growth cannot be considered as a violation of the second law or an increase in complexity of the organism. The original order (full grown adult) had to be created by God. It did not evolve to the ordered state. Once the order is present it can reproduce itself (reproduction and growth).

Another qualitative argument that can be brought to bear against evolution is from a statistical viewpoint. The statistical mechanical approach to entropy[44] is given by

$$S = k \ln w \qquad (27)$$

where S is the entropy, w is the possible number of microstates of a system and k is Boltmann's constant.

For the disordered state, w is very large and for the ordered state it is quite small[45]. It would appear that w would be very small for a living system since no more than a few microstates would be possible. Never at any time could these number of microstates decrease measurably since they would be low already. So there is no realistic way of discussing growth as a means of decreasing w which would then cause a decrease in the entropy content of the organism.

This difference is overlooked by many evolutionists when comparing living and non-living systems. For living systems the number of microstates available should be very small (if the system remains alive). Whereas non-living systems should have many available microstates. Thus the entropy of a living system will always be lower than that of a non-living system, but this order had to be created originally not evolved.

Again, with regard to growth, consider the starting cell, cells, or fertilized egg. It would appear that $w \approx 1$, or any gross rearrangement after fertilization would cause death or degeneration in the growing organism.

However when the organism is full-grown, more possible microstates would be possible such that $w \geq 1$. More microstates could be visualized from the sheer bulk of the system. Also more system contamination could be tolerated in a mature organism and the possible microstates could be increased as a result of this.

This increase in w (number of possible microstates) could be visualized as the different ways of arranging cells with various degrees of difference and various levels of contamination and still have the adult organism remain alive. Thus there will be a decrease in system order with growth, or *no more* than a maintenance of the same order. Certainly no increase in order or complexity should be expected. No rigor is attached to the above argument, but is used simply to illustrate how growth cannot be considered as an ordering procedure.

Often evolutionists claim that decreases in entropy are easily attained[46] and thus evolution from disorder to order is easily possible. The "proof" given for such assertions are examples of reversible processes. For instance the thermal transpiration of gases to develop a pressure gradient under a maintained temperature gradient is sometimes used[47]. The gas in this state has a lower entropy than the initial disordered state with no gradient present. However this steady state has to be maintained by a temperature gradient.

Once the gradient is removed, or given enough time the system would fail, and the gas would return to the original state. If the temperature gradient was reapplied, the pressure gradient would develop. The process is reversible and cannot be compared with a system that has only irreversible processes taking place. It does not approximate a living system. For instance life cannot be reversibly removed and reinstated in a living system. It is impossible to return the living system to some prior state in past time. Again the evolutionary analogy fails.

The temperature gradient mentioned above or any other restraint maintained on the gas system or any other system is not a natural process depending upon random changes only. Such a situation is a controlled process and would not apply to basic evolutionary postulates (random variations). Intelligent beings can set up a system to effect many "ordering" operations, but such ordering cannot be accomplished by natural, "unintelligent" processes.

Sometimes the freezing of water, thawing, refreezing, etc. is used to illustrate how order can be easily obtained. Again this is a reversible process, ice ⇌ liquid. The solid is assumed to have more atomic order than the liquid, and everytime the water solidifies the system order increases. Of course defects in the solid state[48] are ignored in such an argument. However this reversible change can occur over and over again, and no evolution can be observed in the system other than ice ⇌ liquid. How can this be applied to living systems where irreversible changes occur? It is impossible.*

---

*In the above "reversible" change the entropy change of the system plus the entropy change in the surroundings always is positive. The so-called entropy decrease is really artificial when the total analysis is made.

In approaching the problem of evolution using open systems and stationary states, life is already assumed to be present. This is an improper place to start any discussion about the possibility of evolution for it has already been assumed that life spontaneously generated. This faith-postulate has been very neatly avoided. The arguments against evolution become more weighty when inanimate systems are considered, and there is no hope for chemical evolution[49] in face of the second law of thermodynamics.

The problem must always be faced, not avoided, of how did life get here. One cannot talk about evolution in living systems without assuming spontaneous generation and completely ignoring creation. No evolutionist should be allowed to start his argument at such a point and should continually be pushed back to beginnings rather than left alone to assume any starting conditions he wishes.

Negentropy and Living Systems

A great deal of work and study has been done on the idea that the second law does not apply to living systems[50-52], since they exist and feed on a substance called negentropy which allows them to resist the effects of the second law and maintain their high degree of complexity.[53] The system takes in food which is a high-grade energy (low entropy content); it degrades this high energy form to refuse (high entropy) and supposedly lives off of this degradation of the food. This allows the feeder to stabilize and increase its own order. The refuse becomes an entropy sink where the living system can reject excess entropy.

The refuse cannot be an entropy sink and if it is, why can't the "feeder" organism maintain its state of low entropy indefinitely? Why does the organism eventually die? Again the time factor is overlooked in this approach. To consistently use this argument the organism should be able to maintain itself indefinitely. It is questioned that negentropy applies here. It has a definite place in information theory, but when considering this aspect of living systems there will be nothing that the system takes in that will have negentropy.

A simple example will illustrate this. Food coming into any organism has a definite positive entropy content since it is taken from a cursed creation. The digestive processes are irreversible processes and cause an entropy increase within the organism. While food is being degraded the system must work to digest the food. This work generates entropy. Thus there has been an irreversible increase in entropy. If the food was providing a quantity called negentropy, it would be possible for the organism to decrease its entropy content.

Let us follow this process of supposed entropy decrease. As the organism grows and takes in negentropy to grow, it decreases in entropy content. Supposedly, the organism is becoming more and more ordered, attaining more complexity. It is getting better and better. Yet all through the stages of conception, birth and growth to a "stationary" state death is possible. Growing systems die. Indeed, if they are decreasing in entropy, why do they die? The entropy decrease should indicate the organism is being rendered more resistant to changes such as death.

Why, at adulthood, does the organism suddenly stop decreasing in entropy? Why can't this entropy rejection continue until there is a uniform low entropy in all living organisms? Such a process would enable them to maintain this low entropy instead of aging and eventually dying. As can be seen, the analysis may fit a small time in the cycle of a living system, but it is far from complete.

Food intake may allow a system to maintain its present entropy content, or the entropy increase may be very slow for a while, but never can there be any justification for an entropy decrease. Continual ordering or betterment would render death less likely, whereas the probability of death increases with the passage of time for any organism.

Suggesting the introduction of system poisons to cause death does not solve the problem either. This is like "having your cake and eating it too." You want an entropy decrease and you conceptually provide for it. You then want an entropy increase and you provide conceptually for it. The reasoning is not consistent.

It appears that the most consistent approach to the problem is to allow at all stages of life for an increase in entropy. It certainly would not be as rapid as a closed or isolated system but nevertheless it would increase. Once death occurred, the entropy increase would become more rapid. It is felt that this approach would be more consistent with the second law of thermodynamics.

Conclusion

The life principle and order of a living system, etc. was placed in the original kinds at creation. God gave these systems the ability to reproduce this order (fill the earth, after its kind). When sin entered the world, this created order began to decrease; each successive generation containing slightly less order than the previous one. However one must be careful with this analysis for the possibility to replicate this order cannot be completely overcome by the effects of the second law of thermodynamics. This biological conservation is a strong principle, and the increasing disorder from generation to generation in our time appears to be slight.

A great deal has been done by biologists and thermodynamicists to apply thermodynamics to living systems, but an immense amount of additional work needs to be accomplished. Also if evolutionary overtones are maintained as presuppositions, a great deal of the study will be invalidated from the start. Creationists must approach the problem from their standpoint. Always a creationist study must be guided and undergirded by Biblical considerations. Never can Biblical truth be rejected, disregarded or explained away.

So far irreversible themodynamics has been applied mainly to growth of a living organism to adulthood. Weaknesses of this approach have been explored. This is a far cry from any evolutionary development of molecules to man. Creationist alternatives have been suggested. No one can show scientifically that living systems violate the second law of thermodynamics. Only evolutionary interpretation or wishful thinking can suggest this. There is simply not enough scientific information available to substantiate the claim that living systems violate the second law of thermodynamics. Creationist alternatives should be more appealing to Christians. Open systems offer no escape hatch for evolutionists to avoid the second law.

Actually it is not possible to speak of living organisms from a quantitative thermodynamic standpoint. Landsberg[54] states that

There is also no clear understanding yet of the best way of using thermodynamics to elucidate the key properties of living matter. It seems that thermodynamics should have a greater contribution to make than has so far been possible, but there are clearly several major conceptual difficulties to be overcome first.

The complexity of living organisms makes any analysis intractable. This may lead one to the conclusion that life is more than "a sack full of chemicals." The author believes that the complexity of living organisms is a result of creation by God. God's power is shown in His creation. To Him be the Honor and Glory!

REFERENCES
[1]von Bertalanffy, L. 1950. The theory of open systems in physics and biology, *Science,* 111:25.
[2]Crawford, F. H., 1963. Heat, thermodynamics, and statistical physics. Harcourt, Brace, and World, New York, p. 228.
[3]Williams, E. L. 1966. Entropy and the solid state in Why Not Creation? edited by W. E. Lammerts. Creation Research Society Books, 5093 Williamsport Drive, Norcross, GA 30071, pp. 67-79.
[4]Prigogine, I. 1967. Introduction to thermodynamics of irreversible processes. Third Edition. Interscience, New York, p. 16.

[5]Crawford, *Op cit.*, p. 236:

[6]Bridgman, P. W. 1950. The thermodynamics of plastic deformation and generalized entropy, *Review of Modern Physics,* 22:56.

[7]Kestin, J. 1966. A course of thermodynamics. Blaisdell. Waltham, Mass., pp. 132-33.

[8]Bridgman, *Op. cit.* p. 63.

[9]Yourgrau, W., A. van der Merwe, and G. Raw. 1966. Treatise on irreversible and statistical themophysics. Macmillan, New York, p. 2.

[10]*Ibid.*, p. 3.

[11]Fitts, D. D. 1962. Nonequilibrium thermodynamics. McGraw-Hill, New York, pp. 22-24.

[12]Prigogine, I. 1965. Evolution criteria, variational properties, and fluctuations in nonequilibrium thermodynamics, variatonal techniques and stability. Edited by Donnelly, R. J., Herman, R. and Prigogine, I. Univ. of Chicago Press, pp. 3-4.

[13]Fitts, *Op cit.*

[14]Yourgrau, *et. al., Op. cit.*, p. 7.

[15]Williams, *Op. cit.*

[16]Yourgrau, *et al., Op. cit.*, p. 8.

[17]Williams, *Op. cit.*

[18]Williams, E. L. 1970. Is the universe a thermodynamic system?, *Creation Research Society Quarterly,* 7:46.

[19]Prigogine, 1967. *Op. cit.*, p. 16.

[20]Yourgrau, *et. al., Op. cit.*, pp.10-11.

[21]Prigogine, *Op. cit.*, pp. 33-34.

[22]Yourgrau, *et al.*, Op. cit.

[23]Hague, B. 1965. Introduction to vector analysis. Fifth Edition. Methuen, London, p. 39.

[24]*Ibid.*, p. 59.

[25]Prigogine, *Op. cit.*

[26]Yourgrau, *et. al., Op. cit.*, p. 13.

[27]*Ibid.*, p. 16.

[28]Castellan, G. W. 1964. Physical chemistry. Addison-Wesley, Reading, Mass., p. 560.

[29]Yourgrau, *et. al., Op. cit.*, p. 18.

[30]*Ibid.*, p. 23.

[31]Onsager, L. 1931. Recriprocal relations in irreversible processes, *Physical Review,* 37:405, 38:2265.

[32]Yourgrau, *et. al., Op. cit.*, p. 43.

[33]*Ibid*

[34]Tykodi, R. J., 1967. Thermodynamics of steady states. Macmillan, New York, p. 79.

[35]Huxley, J. 1955. Evolution and genetics (in) what is science? Edited by J. R. Newman. Simon & Schuster, New York, p. 278.

[36]Prigogine, *Op. cit.*, p. 17.

[37]*Ibid.*, pp. 75-92.

[38]Yourgrau, *et. al., Op. cit.*, pp. 4853.

[39]von Bertalanffy, *Op. cit.*

[40]von Bertalanffy, L. 1949. Open systems in physics and biology, *Nature,* 163:364.

[41]Prigogine, I. and J. M. Waime. 1946. Biology and thermodynamics of irreversible phenomena, *Experienta,* 2:451.

[42]Kestin, 1967 *Op. cit.*, p. 353.

[43]Prigogine, 1967 *Op. cit.*, p. 92.

[44]Williams, 1966. *Op. cit.*

[45]Williams, *Ibid*

[46]Prigogine, *Op. cit.* p. 92.

[47]Prigogine, *Op. cit.*, pp. 85-87.

[48]Williams 1966, *Op. cit.*

[49]Williams, E. L., 1967. The evolution of complex organic compounds from simple chemical compounds: is it thermodynamically and kinetically possible?, *Creation Research Society Quarterly*, 4:30.

[50]Brillouin, L. 1949. Life, thermodynamics and cybernetics, *American Scientist*, 37:554.

[51]Schrodinger, E. 1945. What is life? Macmillan, New York.

[52]Raymond, R. C. 1950. Communicatin, entropy and life, *American Scientist*, 38:273.

[53]King, A. L. 1962. Thermophysics. W. H. Freeman, San Francisco, p. 253.

[54]Landsberg, P. T. 1970. Thermodynamics makes progress, *Nature,* 225:1206.

III. Thermodynamics and The Creation Model

1

A Proposal For A New Creationist Discipline
Ralph E. Ancil

There are many examples of recent creationist writings suggesting an increasing tendency of researchers to focus on the created kind as a unit with its variations and fixity, rather than examining specific organisms, mutations or natural selection *per se*. Furthermore, diverse arguments, including those of population genetics theory, are brought to bear on the matter. Certainly emphasizing "basic kinds" is not new to the creation model, indeed it is foundational to it; but the arguments fall short of proposing what is proposed here, namely *bararmin*genetics* or creationist population genetics. This new discipline is the counterpart of evolutionary population theory in which the base unit is usually the species to which the *assumed* principle of (macro-) evolution, i.e., unlimited variation, is applied. On the other hand the central feature of baramin genetics is that the created kind is the base unit of investigation to which the *observed* principle of limited variation is applied.[1]

Why has this not been proposed before? There are at least two reasons: (1) there has not been general agreement about the criteria to be used for identifying baramin; and (2) it is quite difficult to recognize baramin in the conventional taxonomic categories. Yet with the recent contributions from creationists, at least the process of clarifying can be started. Perhaps not all baramin can be identified but it is expected that many members from many baramin can be determined at the very least. Research in baramin genetics should help facilitate and stimulate needed research in taxonomy and other related areas.

In baramin genetics the created kinds are viewed in a dual fashion. First, they are seen as biological units in terms of chromosomes, genes and DNA but secondly, they are viewed as sources of genetic information. Although viewing the gene as a source of information is not new, creationists have not made much use of this approach. Bass[2] reports that Lewontin has shown from mathematical genetics that the information content of the genome cannot increase! Surely such an argument as this can be exploited more fully. For example, can it be shown that the information content of the genome, or baramin, actually decreases? By approaching the study of baramin genetics in terms of information, the door is opened to measuring the entropy of the system (baramin) since in a very real sense such information is isolated from that of all other

---

*baramin - from the Hebrew *bara*, create, and *min*, kind; first coined by Marsh; see reference 3.

systems. Thus an important part of creationist biology can be linked to physics via information theory.

Having observed this duality, the following terms are defined: A *baramin* is a group of organisms capable of true fertilization![3,4] Also, it is a group of organisms capable of exchanging information with one another; the gene pool constituting such a group is a pool of information which is mixed or combined. *No exchange of (genetic) information can ever occur between baramin.*

A *variation* is a different way of combining the genetic make-up of the original stock (basic type) so as to produce a novelty. In terms of information content it is the number of distinct ways of combining units of information (alleles) of the original stock.

Degeneration is the loss of variation (or potential for variation) within a baramin. Also, it is the loss of information or the inability to exchange information.

A *point mutation* is a genetic accident, an error of the DNA and is further defined in terms of its biochemistry. Also, it is a *change* of information. Thus a "good" mutation results in an increase of the information content of the baramin; "bad" mutation results in a decrease of the information content; and a "neutral" mutation results in no change of information. Since there is no compelling evidence for a "good" mutation, and since the notion of neutral mutations is a moot question, the creationist may view point mutations as random noise, an interference of the signal, increasing entropy. It is an example of degeneration.

Evolutionists maintain that a mutation is not good or bad *per se*, but is good or bad depending on the environment.[5,6] The famous peppered moth is frequently cited as such an example. Whether or not the difference in colouration is really due to a mutation is a point that can be challenged. Yet by defining mutations in this manner, the evolutionist is also challenged to show not merely that the alleged mutation survives, but more importantly that it has increased the information content (or complexity) of the organism or population *regardless of environment.*

Furthermore, the evolutionist population geneticist must try to find some way of reconciling evolution with increasing entropy. (Although, this writer knows of no such serious effort.) Creationist population genetics is not only fully consistent with the second law, but actually formally includes that law by means of information theory.

Finally, it should be observed that there are undoubtedly many useful results from evolutionary population genetics that can be incorporated into this model. Promising areas of research include population equilibrium, stability, fixation of mutations and so on. Researchers will also require information on such matters as the rates of divergence, the rates of increasing variation and increasing reversion, and the mathematical functions describing these systems. Theoretical input from non-biological areas such as computer and systems engineers can also be used. An example would be the development of computer models to describe the behavior, distribution and variation of baramin.

Summary

A new model has been proposed, baramin genetics, that embraces and formalizes the most fundamental concepts of scientific creationism. The central feature of the discipline is that the created kind is the unit of investigation and applied to that unit is the principle of limited variation. Among its other features is a sort of dual character: results from biology in the form of genetics can be used and results from physics by means of information theory can also be used.

REFERENCES

[1]Marsh, F. L. 1978 Variation and fixity among living things, *Creation Research Society Quarterly* 15(2):118.

[2]Bass, R. W. 1976 Darwin denied: the superstition of stochastic succession, *Creation Research Society Quarterly* 12(4):198.

[3]Marsh, F. L. 1976 Variation and fixity in nature. Pacific Press Publishing Association, Mountain View, California pp. 36, 37.

[4]Siegler, H. R. 1978 A creationists' taxonomy. *Creation Research Society Quarterly* 15(1):37.

[5]Baker and Allen 1971 The study of biology, second edition. Addison and Wesley Publishers. Reading, Massachusetts pp. 697-699.

[6]Patterson, C. 1978 Evolution. Butler and Tanner, Ltd. London p. 83.

2

A Creation Model For Natural Processes

Emmett L. Williams

Types of Natural Processes

An irreducible classification of natural processes* would include three types:

1. Improvement processes—things get better and become more complex
2. Conservation processes—things stay the same
3. Degeneration processes—things get worse, fall apart, and disorder

Assuming all natural processes can be placed into one or two of the above categories,** a logical scientific question to ask is, "Are all of these types of processes possible?" It has been ascertained particularly in the science of thermodynamics that categories 2 and 3 are definitely possible and observable. The interested reader should consult the papers listed in References 1-4 for a technical exposition of the first and second laws of thermodynamics as related to natural processes.

Supposed evolutionary processes fall into category 1. They are impossible and unobservable. This paper is not primarily intended to be a polemic against the philosophy of evolutionary progress.*** The bibliography in Reference 1 may be consulted for such an argument.

The Creationist Model and Conservation Processes

A. Suggested Origin of Conservation Processes—At the end of the six days of creation a fully-functioning, finished physical universe existed. One might ask how did the Creator intend to insure the continuance of His creation? Each day or at certain chosen times God Himself could have appeared in His physical universe and personally attended to it to guarantee that it would operate properly. Or He could have had angels do the janitorial work.

*A natural process is defined as a spontaneous change occurring in nature in a sequence of steps over a period of time.
**A natural process possibly could be a combination of categories, such as 1 and 2, or 2 and 3, but not 1 and 3.
***Natural evolution fits into the general philosophy of progress that is deeply ingrained in human thought and can be traced very easily back to Greek thought. Consider this comment on Aristotle's metaphysical theory.
Everything in the cosmos, from stones, animals, and people up to heavenly bodies, goes through its natural process of change and development in order to approach the perfection, the immutability, of the Unmoved Mover.[5]

Or, He could have set in motion certain physical, chemical, and biological processes to insure the proper continuance of His physical creation. The author suggests the latter possibility as the origin of conservation processes. God ordained them to conserve, maintain, or preserve His creation.

B. Purpose of Conservation Processes — Following the framework of the previous suggestion, conservation processes are the means employed to insure the continuance of the created order.

C. Conservation Processes and Living Organisms—God commanded many living organisms to multiply and fill the earth. This reproduction is after its kind (the phrase "after its kind" is found in Genesis 1:11, 12, 21, 24, 25 in the creation account). Creationists have not been and may not be able to determine the extent of the kind[6-8]. But whatever the kind, it was to reproduce itself. In other words, living organisms were to be *preserved* on the earth through reproduction.

As trite as it may sound, reproduction guarantees conservation of kind. Reproduction, therefore, is a conservation process. Also many maintenance and repair processes in living organisms can be considered conservation processes. These operate so that organisms can continue to reproduce and fill the earth.

As a means of preserving original created order, growth is no more than a conservation process. Many organisms grow to maturity to reproduce to conserve the kind. Also God created fully-mature organisms when He created the earth (creation with apparent age).[9] Thus during growth to maturity the organisms is simply replicating in limited degree the original created order. As the number of organisms increases, the *quantity* of order increases but not the *quality*. Growth, incorrectly, is considered an ordering process by many evolutionists.[10]

D. Conservation Processes and Reproducibility — Conservation of energy, momentum, etc., form a theoretical foundation for much of physics. Likewise conservation of mass forms a foundation for most of chemistry. Scientific conservation laws are laws of prohibition.[11]. It is theoretically possible for anything to happen that is not counter to conservation laws.

Conservation laws depend on certain symmetry properties of the physical universe. For instance, conservation of energy depends upon the symmetry of time. That is, energy can be conserved regardless of when an experiment is performed as long as the experimental conditions are identical. Time is not a variable affecting the outcome of a physical event conducted under identical conditions. If hydrogen gas had been reacted with oxygen gas to form water in 1575, this reaction ($2H_2 + O_2 \xrightarrow{spark} 2H_2O$) would have occurred the same way as in 1675, 1775, 1875, and 1975. Reproducibility is a prime requirement of scientific work.

The author calls this repeatability "conservation of event" for want of better terminology. Four grams of hydrogen combined with 32 grams of oxygen to form water vapor [$2H_2(g) + O_2(g) \rightarrow 2H_2O(g)$] will always yield about 58 kcal. of heat energy. Oak trees will bear acorns which will grow into oak trees which will bear acorns which will grow into oak trees. Dogs will have puppies which will grow into dogs. Humans will have babies which will grow into adults. All of the aforementioned examples can be considered repetitious events.

As the consequence of an orderly operating universe, reproducibility is indirect evidence that an intelligent Being created the universe. It is also a teleological circumstance. Symmetry properties and conservation laws (scientific statement of conservation processes) imply design.[12]

Examples of Conservtion Laws and Symmetry

Conservation Law	Symmetry in Nature
energy	translations in time
linear momentum	translations in space
angular momentum	rotations in space

The Creationist Model and Degeneration Processes

Another type of process observed in nature is degeneration. Things tend to fall apart, living organisms die and decay, and there is a continual drift toward disorder.

When did such a principle become operative in the physical universe? No one can be sure. The Bible is silent, and scientists offer no answers. Any suggested solution is purely conjectural. The author *assumes* that degeneration processes originated at the Fall and unidirectionality in natural processes existed before the Fall.*

Much of this interpretation depends upon the passage "and God saw everything He had made and it was very good" in Genesis 1:31. A state of natural perfection existed with no degeneration—every process operating at 100% efficiency—and with no death in the animal kingdom.

*There has been considerable discussion[13] in past *CRS Quarterlies* about when the second law of thermodynamics came into operation. To clarify the argument, Harold Armstrong[14] suggested that any discussion of the second law should be compartmentalized. Statements of the second law [14, 15] fall into two categories, those dealing with the unidirectionality of natural processes and those dealing with degeneration (the tendency toward disorder).

116

Such a world staggers the mental processes of anyone living in our present world. It is incomprehensible. With the introduction of degeneration processes, nature did not "run" as smoothly. Conservation processes attempt to preserve the created order. However degeneration processes operate countercurrent to any conservation. The net result of degeneration is destruction of order.

The Interrelation of Conservation and Degeneration Processes

A natural "war" ensues in nature, conservation vs. degeneration. Created order is "eroded" by degeneration processes. Conservation processes, however, continually operate to "hold back" degeneration and in many cases may actually overcome the effects of degeneration processes for awhile.

An example will be given to illustrate the interplay of the processes. Lammerts and Howe[16], [17] recently performed some excellent plant succession studies on wildflowers in California. In good years when there was proper rainfall, suitable temperatures, and generally good growing conditions (conservation processes operating efficiently and/or favored by natural conditions), the wildflowers put on a "good show" with many colors per variety, ruffled flowers, lush foliage, etc.

In bad years when there were unfavorable growing conditions (degeneration processes prevailing), the wild flowers were stunted: the blossoms were of the usual color per variety and had no ruffled flowers and less foliage, and many varieties became extinct.

Conservation processes operate more efficiently under conditions suitable to living organisms. Degeneration processes prevail under conditions unsuitable to living organisms, causing them to suffer, die and even become extinct.

What evolutionists attribute to improvement processes is in actuality the result of conservation processes overriding degeneration. The natural changes they would be prone to consider as evolutionary are in reality the result of the interplay of conservation and degeneration processes, by means of which the organisms either degenerates or appears to improve. Any apparent improvement would have to come through genetic recombination or change similar to that observed by Lammerts and Howe.

Which organisms survive? Those that are able to utilize the conservation processes available to them. Those that cannot utilize them cannot cope with the degeneration processes and consequently die out. Struggle does not improve organisms. The less the struggle, the more improved the organisms. Struggle weakens organisms (as Lammerts and Howe have shown).

117

Evolutionists often confront creationists with the following argument. If degeneration processes are so important in the universe, why hasn't everything collapsed into a state of total disorder? This is an excellent question considering the emphasis put on degeneration processes by creationists. The answer is that degeneration processes do not have full sway in the universe. They are opposed by conservation processes. This writer feels that conservation processes are by far the stronger of the two.

It is true that even conservation processes are inefficient. This inefficiency results in a slow deterioration of living organisms. The final result is death for the individual organism. Over a period of time the kinds themselves may degenerate. The order of the universe is slowly being "destroyed" by degeneration processes. However, conservation processes insure that life will continue.

Intelligence aids conservation processes. Man has conquered many diseases and many other things that would have destroyed him. Man in learning about his environment (as he was commanded in Genesis 1:28) has learned how to take care of himself in the face of universal degeneration.

This achievement, coupled with his seemingly remarkable material progress, has lent weight to the idea of evolutionary progress since the Middle Ages. Man appears to be advancing. Yet man is only employing previously ordained conservation processes for his good.

Conclusion

A creationist model for natural processes is superior to any evolutionary model. Nature is minimally a battleground of conservation and degeneration processes. Conservation processes are the stronger of the two. The persistence of order in the universe is due to their superiority, not to improvement processes. Degeneration processes reduce the order in the universe.

REFERENCES

[1]Williams, E. L. 1973. Thermodynamics: a tool for creationists, *Creation Research Society Quarterly* 10(1):38-44.

[2]Williams, E. L. 1974. Living organisms: conservation and degeneration processes. A Challenge to Education: Technical Essays. Second Creation Convention, Milwaukee, August 18-21, 1974. Bible Science Association, Caldwell, Idaho, II B:103-113.

[3]Armstrong, H. L. 1975. Use of the second law of thermodynamics in macroscopic form in Creation studies, *Creation Research Society Quarterly* 12(2):103-106.

[4]Gish, D. T. 1975. A decade of creationist research, *Creation Research Society Quarterly* 12(1):34-46.

[5]Stroll, A., and R. H. Popkin 1972. Introduction to philosophy. Holt, Rinehart, and Winston, Inc., New York, p. 107.

⁶Jones, A. J. 1972. A general analysis of the Biblical "kind" (min), *Creation Research Society Quarterly.* 9(1):53-57.

⁷Jones, A. J. 1972. Boundaries of the min: an analysis of the Mosaic lists of clean and unclean animals, *Creation Research Society Quarterly,* 9(2):114-123.

⁸Jones, A. J. 1973. How many animals in the Ark?, *Creation Research Society Quarterly,* 10(2):102-108.

⁹Whitcomb, J. C., and H. M. Morris 1961. The Genesis Flood. The Presbyterian and Reformed Publishing Co., Philadelphia, pp. 232-239.

¹⁰Williams, E. L. 1971. Resistance of living organisms to the second law of thermodynamics: irreversible processes, open systems, creation, and evolution, *Creation Research Society Quarterly,* 8(2):117-126.

¹¹Ford, K. W. 1963. The world of elementary particles. Xerox Publishing Co., Waltham, Mass., p. 82.

¹²*Ibid.,* pp. 26-27.

¹³Kofahl, R. E. 1973. Entropy prior to the fall, *Creation Research Society Quarterly,* 10(3):154-156. See also the replies by Williams and by Morris immediately following. Also Kofahl, R. E. 1974. Reply concerning entropy prior to the fall, *Creation Research Society Quarterly,* 11(3):175-177, also comments by Jansma, and "In Retrospect" by Armstrong, immediately following. Also White, A. J. 1975. Comments on the nature of things before the fall, *Creation Research Society Quarterly,* 12(2):124, and a letter by Williams, immediately following.

¹⁴Armstrong, H. L. "In Retrospect", mentioned in Reference 15.

¹⁵Williams, E. L. 1973. Reply mentioned in Reference 15.

¹⁶Lammerts, W. E., and G. F. Howe 1974. Plant succession studies in relation to microevolution, *Creation Research Society Quarterly,* 10(4):208-228.

¹⁷Lammerts, W. E. 1974. Plant succession studies in relation to micro-evolution and mutations. A Challenge to Education: Technical Esays. Second Creation Convention, Milwaukee, August 18-21, 1974. Bible-Science Association, Caldwell, Idaho II B:24-31.

IV. Philosophical Perspectives

Thermodynamics and Biblical Theology
Henry M. Morris

Introduction

Instead of the many scientific mistakes and anachronisms alleged by its enemies, the Bible actually contains a remarkable number of passages with modern scientific insights. Of these, none are more significant than the two principles commonly acknowledged to be the most important and most universal of all scientific generalizations. These are the so-called first and second laws of thermodynamics.

The other chapters of this monograph deal with the scientific nature of the two laws, and their implications with respect to the Creation/Evolution issue in science. In this chapter the Biblical and theological aspects are treated, with only enough scientific background to point up their significance.

Like every other scientific "law," these two laws are merely emphirical generalizations based on agreement with a broad range of scientific data. In principle they might even have to be modified or rejected if data should later turn up contradicting them. Nevertheless, they are based on such a tremendous number of supporting measurements, on such a wide variety of types of physical systems, that practically all knowledgeable scientists would recognize them as the most secure of all scientific laws. If there is such a thing as a real *law* in science, these two laws would be the best examples. Despite this fact, however, their real importance and profound implications are commonly ignored or misunderstood by most scientists.

First Law of Thermodynamics

The first law is commonly considered as synonymous with the law of conservation of energy. By "energy" is meant "an entity which does, or has the capacity to do, work." The nation's most prolific science writer, the humanistic biochemist Isaac Asimov defines the first law as follows:

"To express all this, we can say: 'Energy can be transferred from one place to another, or transformed from one form to another, but it can be neither created nor destroyed.' Or we can put it another way: 'The total quantity of energy in the universe is constant.'

This law is considered the most powerful and most fundamental generalization about the universe that scientists have ever been able to make.

No one knows *why* energy is conserved, and no one can be completely sure it is truly conserved everywhere in the universe and under all conditions. All that anyone can say is that in over a century and a quarter of careful measurement, scientists have never been able to point to a definite violation of energy conservation, either in the familiar everyday surroundings about us, or in the heavens above or in the atoms within."[1]

If one regards *mass* as being a type of entity different from energy, then the law can be modified to apply to "the total quantity of energy and mass in the universe," thus allowing for the possibility of energy/mass conversions. Except for the latter, of course, mass also is universally conserved.

In addition, there are still other conservation laws in physics (e.g., momentum, electric charge), not to mention the universally observed principle in biology that "like begets like" (that is, the basic kinds of plants and animals reproduce only their own kinds, never some new kind). It seems beyond question that the world as science knows it is a world in which existing basic entities are always *conserved*, never *created* or *annihilated* (the phenomenon of extinction in biology may seem to be an exception, but it should be remembered that in genetics, it is the *code* which is conserved, not the individual or even the "kind" built up around that code).

Second Law of Thermodynamics
The second law is expressed in a number of different ways, all of which are essentially equivalent to each other. Again calling on Asimov (no creationist or theist, but an evolutionary humanist) for an unbiased definition, he speaks of it this way:
"We can say: 'No device can deliver work unless there is a difference in energy concentration within the system, no matter how much total energy is used.'
That is one way of stating what is called the second law of thermodynamics. It is one of many ways; all of them are equivalent although some very sophisticated mathematics and physics is involved in showing the equivalence."[2]

Asimov then goes on to give another very picturesque definition:
"Another way of stating the second law, then, is: 'The universe is constantly getting more disorderly.'

Viewed that way, we can see the second law all about us. We

121

have to work hard to straighten a room, but left to itself, it becomes a mess again very quickly and very easily. Even if we never enter it, it becomes dusty and musty. How difficult to maintain houses, and machinery, and our own bodies in perfect working order; how easy to let them deteriorate. In fact, all we have to do is nothing, and everything deteriorates, collapses, breaks down, wears out, all by itself—and that is what the second law is all about."[3]

Universal Application

The second law, obviously, is no less universal than the first. *Everything* deteriorates—all by itself! Furthermore, just as with the first law, no one knows *why* this is true—it just always works that way. Asimov was referring specifically to the "universe" as getting more disorderly, just as he had said it was for the universe that the total quantity of energy was a constant.

In a so-called "open system," of size less than the universe, there can for a while, of course, be an influx of energy or mass or order into that system, at the expense of decreased energy, etc., outside the system, but this is superficial. The conditions under which such an apparent exception to one of the laws can occur has been discussed at length in earlier chapters. For present purposes, we can stipulate the range of application of the two laws as follows:

(1) To the universe as a whole, applicable without exception, so far as any scientific observation can determine.

(2) To a local isolated system within the universe, applicable without exception, so far as all scientific measurements have shown.

(3) To a local "open" system, directly applicable in most situations and always applicable as a *normal tendency* in the system, with exceptions possible only under certain special conditions as described elsewhere, and then only at the cost of offsetting external conditions which maintain the integrity of the two laws in the universe as a whole.

Entropy

In connection with the second law, it is necessary also to define the term "entropy." The entropy of a system is usually expressed mathematically, and so is difficult to define precisely without reference to the mathematical description of a particular system. In general, however, entropy can be defined as a mathematical function which quantifies the "disorder" or "unavailable energy" (other terms—might be used, depending on the type of system) in the system. In any case, the second law states that the entropy of any system either increases (if isolated, or universal) or *tends* to increase (if local and open).

Furthermore, as Asimov noted, there are several ways to describe the second law (or its measure, entropy) all of them equivalent and interchangeable. In physical systems, for example, it is commonly expressed in three ways.

(1) As a measure of the increasing unavailability of the energy of the system for useful work *(Classical Thermodynamics).*

(2) As a measure of the increasing disorder, randomness or probability of the arrangement of the components of the system *(Statistical Thermodynamics).*

(3) As a measure of the increasingly confused information in the transmission of the coded message through a system *(Informational Thermodynamics).*

Entropy thus can measure the useless energy in a working system, the disorder in a structured system, or the "noise" in an information system. All use the same types of mathematical formulations, so all are essentially equivalent.

The concept can be extended still further. In biological systems, the phenomena of sickness, death and extinction represent outworkings of the second law. In social and economic systems, the tendency of once-vigorous societies to atrophy and disintegrate is another example. In religious systems, the tendency of faiths which were once strong and dynamic to become lethargic and apostate is still another.

Thus, it is evident that the first and second laws of thermodynamics are exceedingly important universal principles. Far from being limited to the study of heat engines, as the name might imply, they represent broad categories of phenomena throughout the whole of human experience. And a universal effect requires a universal cause!

Theological Implications

Consider, for the time being, only the theological implications of the two laws for the universe as a whole. A superficial application of the first law would conclude that the mass/energy of the universe is eternal, since none is being either created or annihilated within the natural processes which obey the law. A superficial application of the second law would imply a future death of the universe (not its annihilation, but the cessation of all processes and complete disorder), since the universe is now proceeding inexorably in that direction.

But the real testimony of the two laws is profoundly teleological. If matter had really been functioning eternally in the manner described by the two laws, the universe would *already* be dead. Its present unrestrained progress in the direction of decay has been called *Time's Arrow,* and the arrow points down! The future fate of the universe has frequently been called its inevitable eventual "heat death," when the sun and stars have all burned out and all the high-level energy in the cosmos has been degraded to heat at a uniformly low temperature throughout all space. The energy will not have been annihilated, but will be at constant level everywhere, so that no more work can be done.

Now since the universe is not yet "dead," and since it is going to die in time, it is obvious that "Time" had a beginning! If time had extended infinitely into the past, the universe already would be dead. Thus, the second law testifies conclusively that the universe of Time, Space and Matter (the universe is a "continuum," so Space and Matter must be contemporaneous with Time), in its present form at least, must have had a beginning at "Zero Time."

The first law, on the other hand, unequivocally stipulates that the universe could not have begun itself! The second law says there must have been a creation, but the first law says the universe could not create itself.

The only way out of this impasse is to recognize that "in the beginning God created the heaven and the earth." Genesis 1:1 is the most profoundly scientific statement ever written, with all the systems and processes of the cosmos uniting in asserting its truth. The two laws of thermodynamics, the best-proved, most universal generalizations of science, embrace all the processes of nature within their framework, standing as a continuing testimony that the universe as it now exists must have had a beginning and that the Cause of the universe must have been transcendent to it, capable of creating an entire universe, infinite in extent, unending in duration, and boundless in variety and complexity.

This great First Cause must have been able to create all the complex of effects permeating the Space/Mass/Time cosmos. These include an endless array of intelligible complex systems, stars and suns in almost infinite number and power, a tremendous variety of living organisms, and human beings who think, feel, will and love. The two laws can thus be sublimated into the great Law of Cause-and-Effect, with a clear testimony that the uncaused First Cause of the universe must be an infinite, eternal, omnipotent, omniscient, living, willing, loving Person. "In the beginning, God."

Escape from Science

The universal theistic implications of the two laws thus clearly confirm the profound assertion of Genesis 1:1. Since both science and Scripture unite in pointing to a transcendent God as primeval Creator of all things, one can escape from this conclusion only by appealing to evolutionary metaphysics.

It is one thing, however, to repudiate Scripture with philosophy, and quite another to reject science at the same time. In a science-oriented society, this can only be done by so masking the metaphysics as to make it *appear* scientific. This is exactly what evolutionary "cosmogonists" have essayed to do with their "steady-state" and "big bang" cosmogonies.

The problem is the second law. All *observed* processes and systems operating in space and time obey the second law, which thus points back to a creative origin of all such *natural* processes and systems (or, more fundamentally, energy and mass), as well as space and time themselves, by what must have been a *supernatural* event or process.

This unwelcome conclusion can be avoided, however, by postulating that some process or system operating in either *non-observable space* or *non-observable time* may be able by "naturalistic" means to overcome the second law. The first assumption (second law negated by a naturalistic process functioning in non-observable space) leads to some form of the so-called "Steady State Theory." The second assumption (second law negated by a naturalistic process functioning in non-observable time) leads to some form of the so-called "Big Bang Theory."

By their very nature, these so-called theories cannot really be scientific theories since the processes on which they depend cannot possibly be observed. In all observable space and time, all natural processes conform to the second law. To negate the second law requires, therefore, processes which are anti-natural. Evolutionary metaphysicians may enjoy playing semantic games in order to escape from the conclusion of primeval *creative supernatural processes* but all they have in their place are *imaginary anti-natural processes!*

It is encouraging that at least some evolutionary cosmogonists acknowledge this aspect of their speculations, though most of them continue to mask their anti-scientific presuppositions with an imposing mathematical apparatus to make their efforts seem scientific.

The steady-state cosmology is currently out of favor with almost all cosmogonists, so we need not elaborate on it here. Sufficient to say that its version of anti-natural processes (e.g., continuous "creation" of hydrogen atoms or some other form of matter or energy out of *nothing* (!) somewhere deep in interstellar space) violates *both* laws of thermodynamics.

During the past decade, practically all evolutionary astronomers have gone over to some form of "Hot Big Bang" cosmogony. For our purposes here, it is enough to note that this assumption still entails processes which not only are non-observable but also are anti-natural, proceeding in fashion contrary to that specified by the second law. A well-known writer on mathematical astrophysics and cosmogony, Paul C. W. Davies, of the King's College in London, has recently made this point in a remarkable article in a new scientific journal. Professor Davies first points out the very problem we have been discussing.

"The greatest puzzle is where all the order in the universe came from originally. How did the cosmos get wound up, if the second law of thermodynamics predicts asymmetric unwinding toward disorder?—There is good evidence that the primeval universe was not ordered, but highly chaotic: a relic of the primordial chaos survives in a curious radiation from space, believed to be the last fading remnant of the primeval heat, and the characteristics of its spectrum reveal that in the earliest moments of the universe the cosmological material was completely unstructured."[4]

Thus not only is the primeval explosion not scientifically observable but also the very data (e.g., expanding universe, background radiation, energies available for nucleosynthesis, etc.) which seem to offer a quasi-scientific rationale for postulating the big bang, still further support the inferences of the second law, and so offer little prospect of energizing the entire future evolutionary development of the cosmos.

The only hope apparently lies in the first few minutes of the expansion, when the energies and densities were (possibly) sufficiently high as to act in opposition to the second law. Dr. Davies continues his analysis thus:

"To discover the cosmic winding mechanism, one has to investigate the processes that occurred between about one second and ten minutes after the bang. Unfortunately, the expansion is now too sluggish to have much invigorating effect, so the universe seems doomed to steadily unwind again until all organized activity ceases; the interesting and varied world of our experience will be systematically destroyed."[5]

But how can we deduce a naturalistic winding-up process for the universe when all observable naturalistic processes are unwinding processes? Well, as a matter of fact, admits Davies, we can't!

"So far it has been supposed that the shuffling process—is *random*. But how do we know that the universe which emerged from the big bang was truly chaoitic so that subsequent collisions between atoms and interactions between subatomic particles are overwhelmingly likely to disintegrate any order which may appear? If the miracle of the big bang included *miraculously* organized subatomic arrangements too, then random shuffling would have to be replaced by *organized* rearranagement."[6]

There is the answer! We must have the *"miracle* of the big bang," and *"miraculously* ordered subatomic arrangments," with *organized* rearrangement" of the sub-atomic particles!

Yes, a sufficiently comprehensive miracle of supernatural creation and integration might make the "Big Bang" concept workable, but there is no naturalistic way it can be done. And if we are going to acknowledge a miraculous creation at the beginning of things, by what possible logic (even metaphysical dissimulation) can we preclude a miraculous Creator?

And, then, if we acknoweldge a supernatural Creator at all, why not allow Him to do the work of creating and organizing the cosmos all at once, getting right to the implementation of His purposes for creating it in the first place? Why force Him to drag it out over tortuous aeons, merely in order to accommodate evolutionary speculations for which there is not one iota of either scientific or Scriptural evidence? If the Creator actually employed unknown billions of years of universal decay, to allow a primordial ten minutes of miraculous integration to eventually produce man "in His own image," then He certainly selected the most wasteful, inefficient cruel process that could be conceived to accomplish His goal.

The fact is that absolutely all the solid data of both true science and true logic coincide perfectly with the Biblical premise: "In the beginning God created the heaven and the earth." (Genesis 1:1). Supporting this clear foundational statement are many other unequivocal assertions of Scripture:

"By the word of the Lord were the heavens made; and all the host of them by the breath of His mouth.—For He spake, and it was done; He commanded, and it stood fast." (Psalm 33:6, 9).
"For He commanded, and they were created." (Psalm 148:5).
"Through faith we understand that the worlds were framed by the word of God, so that things which are seen were not made of things which do appear." (Hebrews 11:3).
"By the word of God the heavens were of old, and the earth" (II Peter 3:5).
"In six days the Lord made heaven and earth, and on the seventh day, He rested, and was refreshed." (Exodus 31:17).

Origin of the Two Laws According to Scripture
As admitted by Isaac Asimov, "no one knows *why* energy is con-

served." Neither does anyone know why entropy increases. All we know is that, in all scientific measurements and observations, energy is conserved and entropy increases, and there are no known exceptions. These are the two best-proved and most universally, applicable generalizations of science, but no one knows *why!*

That is, no one knows why, scientifically. Theologically and Biblically, however, the reasons why are clear and definite. Not only did Scripture long anticipate the *fact* of the two laws, but also the reasons *why* they are laws.

Consider the first law. The reason *why* no energy is now being created is that "on the seventh day God ended His work which He had made;—in it He had rested from all His work which God created and made." (Genesis 2:2-3).

Similarly, the reason why nothing is being annihilated in the present cosmos is that the Creator (none other than the eternal Son of God, the Lord Jesus Christ) is now "upholding all things by the word of His power." (Hebrews 1:3).

During the six days of creation, God was creating and making all things. Obviously, therefore, the first law was not yet "enacted." When God "ended His work,"however, the whole universe was "very good" (Genesis 1:31). Nothing further needed to be added, nor did anything need correction. Consequently, on God's first great Rest Day (the Hebrew *sabbath* means "rest"), God, as it were, legislated his law of conservation, and the processes of the cosmos have obeyed it ever since!

As a matter of fact, not only were the created energy and matter intended for conservation following the creation week, but so was entropy. Everything was "good," so the entities measured by entropy (disorder, lost energy, noise, disintegration, confusion, wear, death, etc.) could not have been increasing then as they are today. Decay and death are not good.

During the creation period, God was "forming" (Hebrew *yatsar*) and "making" *(asah)* things, as well as "creating" *(bara)*. Thus, His processes then were explicitly opposite to those now constrained by the two laws. His processes then were processes of *creation* and *integration*; now all processes are processes of *conservation* and *disintegration*. God was producing order and complexity, as well as energy and matter, during creation week, and all of these were certainly intended to be conserved following creation week.

This fact in no way implies, however, that there was to be no decrease in order in individual systems. For example, God specifically prepared the grasses, herbs and fruits of the plant kingdom to serve as foods for both people and animals (Genesis 1:29, 30; 2:9, 16). The eating of these foods did, of course, involve the various processes of ingestion and digestion with a corresponding disintegration of the structure of the particular fruit or vegetable (fruits, incidentally, do not "die" when eaten, since they do not possess the *nephesh*, or "soul," or "life," as usually translated from the Hebrew; only men and animals were invested with *nephesh*-see Genesis 1:21; 2:7).

In the primeval creation, however, even though what we might call "decay" processes certainly existed (e.g., digestion, friction, water erosion, wave attenuation, etc.), they must all have balanced precisely with "growth" processes elsewhere either within the individual system or, perhaps more commonly, in an adjacent system, so that the entropy of the world as a whole would stay constant. The entropy of the universe now is increasing, but ideally it should be conserved along with energy. Every process and machine would then have 100% efficiency, with all input energies being converted completely into useful work. Even the heat energy employed in processes necessitating the force of friction for their operation would be completely productive, with no energy being "lost." No parts would wear out, no organism would "age" past the point of maximum vigor and productivity, and everyone could easily design and build perpetual motion machines!

The above is obviously imaginative, and no doubt imprecise and incomplete, but it could not be too far off. Everything was designed by an omniscient, omnipotent God to be "very good." The first law would have stated, as at present, the conservation of mass/energy in all systems and the second law the conservation of entropy in all systems.

But there has been a drastic amendment to the second law! No death of sentient life, either animal or human, was intended in God's original creation. Animal flesh as well as human flesh—and indeed all things in God's physical creation—had been formed by God out of the "dust of the earth" (the basic elementary particles that function in the space/time universe) into a tremendous variety of complex systems, the most complex of all being man's body and brain.

But now everything is proceeding back again to the dust, according to the second law of thermodynamics. "For we know that the whole creation groaneth and travaileth in pain together until now" (Romans 8:22).

The question: "Why?" once again can only be answered theologically, and the Biblical answer is Man's sin and God's curse. God had warned Adam and Eve that death would result from disobedience to His Word (Genesis 2:16, 17) but they chose to believe Satan's word rather than God's Word, and thus brought death into the world. The formal announcement of the second law in its post-Fall form is found in Genesis 3:17-20: "Cursed is the ground for thy sake: in sorrow shalt thou eat of it all the days of thy life; thorns also and thistles shall it bring forth to thee, and thou shalt eat the herb of the field; In the sweat of thy face shalt thou eat bread, till thou return unto the ground; for out of it wast thou taken; for dust thou art, and unto dust shalt thou return." The curse extended in like form to all of man's dominion. Man had brought spiritual disorder into his own dominion; God appropriately imposed a principle of physical disorder on that dominion as befitting its spiritual condition.

The divine curse was not only punitive, but also pedagogical. It was "for man's sake." A world in which there was no judgment for sin, no struggle to survive and no contemplation of suffering and death would be suitable only for beings wholly in fellowship with their Creator. For creatures who had deliberately broken that fellowship, however, such a perfect world could only encourage them to persist in that rebellion and even to intensify it, forever.

Thus, as best we can understand both Scripture and science, we must date the establishment of the second law of thermodynamics, in its present form at least, from the tragic day on which Adam sinned, and when "by man came death" (I Corinthians 15:21). "Therefore, as by one man sin entered into the world, and death by sin; and so death passed upon all men, for that all have sinned" (Romans 5:12).

Not only is the curse pedagogical but also eschatological. Although it points forward to a future heat death of the universe, it also points backward to a purposeful Creator who would never allow the universe to die! "For the creation was made subject to vanity (or better, "futility"), not willingly, but by reason of Him who hath subjected the same in hope. Because the creation itself also shall be delivered from the bondage of corruption (literally "decay") into the glorious liberty of the children of God" (Romans 8:20, 21).

There is a great day coming when "there shall be no more curse" (Revelation 22:3). In the present age, however, ever since Eden, "the whole creation groaneth and travaileth in pain" (Romans 8:22).

Biblical References to First Law

In addition to the fundamental statements already cited from Scripture establishing the completeness and permanence of the creation, there are numerous other references in the Bible to this principle of conservation. These are not couched in technical jargon, of course, since this would change from generation to generation, but in terms of the timeless concept that God safeguards His finished creation, enabling it to accomplish His purposes in every part. Listed below, in outline form, are a few of the passages asserting one or another aspect of the great principle of the conservation of God's finished creation.

130

A. *Passages Asserting God's Rest from a Finished Creation.*
 (1) "Thus the heavens and the earth were finished, and all the host of them. And on the seventh day God ended His work which He had made; and He rested on the seventh day from all His work which He had made. And God blessed the seventh day and sanctified it: because that in it He had rested from all His work which God created and made." (Genesis 2:1-3).
 (2) "For in six days the Lord made heaven and earth, the sea, and all that in them is, and rested the seventh day: wherefore the Lord blessed the sabbath day, and hallowed it." (Exodus 20:11).
 (3) "For in six days the Lord made heaven and earth, and on the seventh day, He rested and was refreshed." (Exodus 31:17).
 (4) "The works were finished from the foundation of the world. For He spake in a certain place of the seventh day on this wise And God did rest the seventh day from all His works" (Hebrews 4:3, 4).
 (5) "For he that is entered into his rest, he also hath ceased from his own works, as God did from His" (Hebrews 4:10).

To the above texts could be added a very large number of references referring to God's works of creation, *all of which are in the past tense* (e.g., Colossians 1:16). It is significant that the Bible never refers to the creation of either the physical universe or the living creatures in it as a work which is continuing today. It is always presented as completed in the past, exactly as implied by the laws of thermodynamics.

B. *Passages Indicating God's Preservation of the Finished Creation.*
 (1) "Thou hast made heaven, the heaven of heavens, with all their host, the earth, and all things that are therein, the seas, and all that is therein, and thou preservest them all" (Nehemiah 9:6).
 (2) "Lift up your eyes on high, and behold who hath created these things—for that He is strong in power; not one faileth!" (Isaiah 40:26).
 (3) "Every good gift and every perfect gift is from above, and cometh down from the Father of lights, with whom is no variableness, neither shadow of turning" (James 1:17).
 (4) "And He is before all things, and by Him all things consist (literally 'are sustained')" (Colossians 1:17).
 (5) "The heavens and the earth, which are now, by the same word are kept in store" (II Peter 3:7).
 (6) "Who being the brightness (literally 'out-radiating') of His glory, and the express image of His person and upholding all

things by the word of His power." (Hebrews 1:3).

(7) "He hath also stablished them for ever and ever: He hath made a decree which shall not pass" (Psalm 148:6).

C. *Passages Asserting Permanence of the Created Kinds of Organisms.*

(1) "God said, Let the earth bring forth grass, the herb yielding seed, and the fruit tree yielding fruit after his kind, whose seed is in itself, upon the earth, and it was so."

(2) "And God created great whales, and every living creature that moveth, which the waters brought forth abundantly, after their kind, and every winged fowl after his kind." (Genesis 1:21).

(3) "And God made the beast of the earth after his kind, and cattle after their kind, and every thing that creepeth upon the earth after his kind" (Genesis 1:25).

(4) "Can the fig tree, my brethren, bear olive berries? either a vine figs? so can no fountain both yield salt water and fresh" (James 3:12).

(5) "That which thou sowest, thou sowest not that body that shall be, but bare grain, it may chance of wheat or of some other grain: But God giveth it a body as it hath pleased Him, and to every seed his own body. All flesh is not the same flesh: but there is one kind of flesh of men, another flesh of beasts, another of fishes, and another of birds." (I Corinthians 15:37–39).

Whether or not the scientific principle of conservation of mass/energy can eventually be demonstrated to incorporate the principle of conservation of the genetic code for each created "kind" is a subject for future creationist research, but the principle of divine conservation of the completed creation beautifully covers both, and all known facts of either physical or biological science agree.

D. *Passages Summarizing Both Completion and Permanence.*

(1) "the thing that hath been, it is that which shall be; and that which is done is that which shall be done: and there is no new thing under the sun. Is there any thing whereof it may be said. See, this is new? It hath been already of old time, which was before us." (Ecclesiastes 1:9, 10).

(2) "I know that, whatsoever God doeth, it shall be forever; nothing can be put to it, nor any thing taken from it; and God doeth it, that men should fear before Him. That which hath been is now; and that which is to be hath already been; and God requireth that which is past" (Ecclesiastes 3:14, 15).

(3) "(He) hath measured the waters in the hollow of His hand, and meted out heaven with the span, and comprehended the dust of the earth in a measure, and weighed the mountains in scales, and the hills in a balance" (Isaiah 40:12).

Biblical References to the Second Law

The Bible refers to the decay principle almost as often as the conservation principle. The basic passage, as noted earlier, is Genesis 3:14-19, recording the divine curse on the whole creation because of the rebellion of its human masters, Adam and Eve.

As noted earlier, the entropy principle is very broad, referring to the loss of useful energy, the loss of order, or the loss of information. It applies to all processes, both inorganic and living, and many are applying it today to social and economic systems as well. Similarly the Bible indicates that the process of decay is universal.

A. *Passages Referring to Decay of the Whole Cosmos.*

(1) "Of old hast thou laid the foundation of the earth; and the heavens are the work of thy hands. They shall perish, but thou shalt endure; yea, all of them shall wax old like a garment; as a vesture shalt thou change them, and they shall be changed. But thou art the same, and thy years shall have no end" (Psalm 102:25-27). (See also Hebrews 1:10-12).

(2) "Lift up your eyes to the heavens and look upon the earth beneath: for the heavens shall vanish away like smoke, and the earth shall wax old like a garment, and they that dwell therein shall die in like manner: but my salvation shall be for ever, and my righteousnes shall not be abolished" (Isaiah 51:6).

(3) "Heavens and earth shall pass away (literally 'are passing away'), but my words shall not pass away" (Matthew 24:35), (See also Mark 13:31 and Luke 21:33).

(4) "And the world passeth away (literally 'is passing away'), and the lust thereof: but he that doeth the will of God abideth forever" (I John 2:17).

(5) "And this word, Yet once more, signifieth the removing of those things that are shaken, as of things that are made, that those things which cannot be shaken may remain" (Hebrews 12:27).

(6) "For the creation was made subject to vanity, not willingly, but by reason of Him who hath subjected the same in hope. Because the creation itself also shall be delivered from the bondage of corruption into the glorious liberty of the children of God. For we know that the whole creation groaneth and travaileth in pain together until now" (Romans 8:20-22).

B. *Passages Indicating Decay of All Living Organisms.*

(1) "Man that is born of woman is of few days, and full of trouble. He cometh forth like a flower, and is cut down: he fleeth also as shadow, and continueth not" (Job 14:1, 2).

(2) "As for man, his days are as grass: as a flower of the field, so he flourisheth. For the wind passeth over it, and it is gone; and the place thereof shall know it no more" (Psalm 103:15, 16).

(3) "For that which befalleth the sons of men befalleth beasts, even one thing befalleth them: as the one dieth, so dieth the other; yea, they have all one breath; so that a man hath no preeminence above a beast: for all is vanity. All go unto one place; all are of the dust, and all turn to dust again" (Ecclesiastes 3:19, 20).

(4) "All flesh is grass, and all the goodliness thereof is as the flower of the field: The grass withereth, the flower fadeth: because the spirit of the Lord bloweth upon it: surely the people is grass. The grass withereth, the flower fadeth; but the word of our God shall stand forever" (Isaiah 40:6–8). (See also I Peter 1:24, 25).

C. *Passages Asserting Personal Decay.*

(1) "Even the youths shall faint and be weary, and the young man shall utterly fall: But they that wait upon the Lord shall renew their strength" (Isaiah 40:30, 31).

(2) "For all our days are passed away in thy wrath: we spend our years as a tale that is told. The days of our years are threescore years and ten; and if by reason of strength they be fourscore years, yet is their strength labour and sorrow; for it is soon cut off, and we fly away" (Psalm 90:9, 10).

(3) "But I see another law in my members, warring against the law of my mind, and bringing me into captivity to the law of sin which is in my members. O wretched man that I am! Who shall deliver me from the body of this death" (Romans 7:23, 24).

(4) "Then when lust hath conceived, it bringeth forth sin: and sin, when it is finished, bringeth forth death" (James 1:15).

It will be noted that, in many of the above passages, the decay of the particular system in view (be it cosmic, biological or human) is often set in contrast with the stability and permanence of its Creator and the spiritual gifts which he provides. The one who enacted the law of decay is, by that very fact, not bound by it Himself.

Although the second law presents the whole universe in a state of decay, the one who created the universe and established its laws is above the universe and not bound by its laws. The grass withers, but the Word of God stands. Though the earth shall wax old like a garment, God's salvation shall be forever. The world is passing away, but they who do the will of God abide. Even the young men faint, but those who wait on the Lord renew their strength.

There is a succinct and wonderful passage in the Bible describing the primeval "winding-up" of the cosmos. The universe has been "running down" ever since Adam's fall, but this required that it first be wound up. The tremendous energy of the universe must first be empowered by God before it can be dissipated. The beautiful order of the creation must be designed and structured before it can run down to disorder. The infinite complexity of the cosmos and the information required for its operation must be planned and encoded before it can become distorted and confused. All three of these aspects of the cosmos are summarized in Isaiah 40:26:

"Lift up your eyes on high, and behold who hath created these things, that bringeth out their host by number: He calleth them all by names by the greatness of His might, for that He is strong in power; not one faileth."

Note: God brings out the host of entities in the cosmos by "number" (that is, in perfect *order*): He identifies them all by specific names appropriate to their intended functions (that is, invested with complete *information*): and He invests them all with unfailing power (that is, renewable *energy*).

In this present world, systems may become confused and disorderd and feeble. But not their Creator!

"Hast thou not known! hast thou not heard, that the everlasting God, the Lord, the Creator of the ends of the earth, fainteth not, neither is weary? there is no searching of His understanding" (Isaiah 40:29).

And then, in one of the most beautiful passages in all language, the chapter closes with the assurance that this same infinite energy, order and information are available to all those men and women who, as "open systems" open their hearts and lives to Him:

"He giveth power to the faint; and to them that have no might He increaseth strength. Even the youths shall faint and be weary, and the young men shall utterly fall: But they that wait upon the Lord shall renew their strength; they shall mount up with wings as eagles: they shall run, and not be weary; and they shall walk, and not faint" (Isaiah 40:29–31).

135

Miraculous Exceptions to the Two Laws

The first and second laws of thermodynamics apply to all *natural* processes, and thus any exception to one or both the laws would require a *supernatural* process. This fact provides the best definition and test of the miraculous. That is, a miracle can be defined as any event whose occurrence requires suspension of one or both of the two laws. Essentially, a miracle would involve the special creation of energy, mass, and/or complexity.

For example, consider the seven great miracles, or "signs," that provide the basic expositional framework for the Gospel of John. Each of these was a true miracle of creation, as follows:

(1) *Water transmuted into wine* (John 2:1-11). The simple molecular structure of water became the far more complex structure of wine, requiring instantaneous creation of complexity, or information.

(2) *The dying son healed* (John 4:46-54). An instantaneous reversal of the decay process, restoring to full vigor and activity the cellular structure that had been destroyed by a mortal illness, was accomplished merely by a spoken word uttered over ten miles away.

(3) *The crippled man made whole* (John 5:3-9). A man unable to walk for 38 years instantaneously received strong, firm legs at Jesus' command, involving the creation of new bone, muscle and other components in place of the atrophied, dead members.

(4) *The multitude fed* (John 6:5-13). The law of mass conservation was suspended while Jesus transposed five loaves and two fishes into bread and meat more than sufficient for five thousand men.

(5) *Gravity superseded* (John 6:16-21). The law of energy conservation was set aside as the Lord Jesus created an anti-gravitational force of unknown nature, enabling Him to walk along the surface of a stormy sea.

(6) *The blind made to see* (John 9:1-7). Both matter and complexity were instantly created when a man blind from birth suddenly possessed perfectly functioning eyes in his previously empty eye sockets.

(7) *The dead restored to life* (John 11:33-44). Not only were the limbs and eyes dead, but the whole body in this case, and for four whole days, so that putrefaction had set in. Nevertheless, at the creative word of Christ, all cells and functions were instantly restructured and reprogrammed, and even the departed spirit summoned again to the body, so that Lazarus lived.

Since all of these were mighty miracles of creation, and since only God can create, the testimony of John 20:30-31 is an understandably strong assertion of the deity of Christ.

"And many other signs truly did Jesus in the presence of His disciples, which are not written in this book: But these are written that ye might believe that Jesus is the Christ, the Son of God; and that believing ye might have life through His name."

Many of the Bible miracles (though not all, by any means) are similar miracles of creation, requiring the suspension of one or both the two laws of thermodynamics, and testifying to the direct power of God the Creator. Examples from the Old Testament, drawn more or less at random, might include the following:

(1) Creation of mass: the miracle of the increasing oil (II Kings 4:1-6).

(2) Creation of energy: the restrained walls of water at the Red Sea crossing (Exodus 14:29).

(3) Creation of complexity: the multiplied languages, with implied corresponding brain structures relating to the varied phonologies at the Tower of Babel (Genesis 11:1-9).

Another form of creative miracle is the impartation of divine "information" to man. Sometimes this information has come through dreams or visions, sometimes by direct theophanic revelation. More commonly, it came by less immediate and obvious ways, but no less real and effective, as "holy men of God spake as they were moved by the Holy Ghost" (II Peter 1:21).

Many of the healings described in the Bible (though not all) seem to have involved divine creative activity and thus to have been real miracles of creation. An example would be the healing of Naaman's leprosy after he had dipped his body seven times in the Jordan (II Kings 5:1-14). There are no medicinal powers to cure leprosy, either in river water or in psychosomatic suggestion. What amounted to new flesh must have been created for Naaman by God in answer to Elisha's prayer.

But the greatest of all miracles of creation was the creation itself, when God brought into existence and completion all the matter and energy and complexity of the entire universe. And the greatest of all delusions is the belief that all of this could be accomplished by anything *other* than creation! If evolution is true, there must have been a miracle of creation interjected at every stage of evolutionary growth from one level of complexity to the next. *Natural* processes are governed by the second law of thermodynamics, which stipulates that these processes normally proceed in a direction exactly opposite to the direction required by evolution. They go downhill instead of uphill, and this can be reversed only on a limited basis under special conditions never satisfied by any evolutionary processes ever observed (e.g., innate evolutionary programming and "negentropy" generators).

In addition to miracles of creation, the Bible records many remarkable phenomena which might also be considered miraculous, except that they did not require suspension of one of the laws of thermodynamics. Rather, they represent unusual combinations of the factors that control the location or rate of an event or process. Every event that occurs in our space/time universe is brought about by a combination of many factors which determine its time, its location and its speed of occurrence. If any of the factors vary, then the event is affected in either place of occurrence, time of occurrence, or rate of occurrence. Every process, or class of events, thus functions statistically around an average and within a range, determined by the variability of the various factors affecting it.

Now, if a certain type of event, or particular process, is observed to occur near the outer limits of its scope of applicability, it will have a very small probability of such occurrence and might be considered so unusual as to be called a miracle even though it operates within the constraints of the laws of thermodynamics. Biblical examples would include such events as the overnight deaths of 185,000 Assyrians (II Kings 19:35), the survival of Daniel through a long night in a den of hungry lions (Daniel 6:16-24), the deliverance of Peter from his shackles and prison (Acts 12:5-11), and many others.

In the above examples, the Bible indicates that God actually sent an angel to control the arrangement of the factors governing the event. It may be that many such "miracles of providence" (distinguished from "miracles of creation") are likewise influenced by angelic manipulation of one or more parameters affecting the particular process.

Neither angels nor demons, nor human beings can truly *create*, since they themselves are creatures, not the Creator, and hence cannot (without direct empowering from God) perform creative miracles, but they evidently can, under many circumstances, so manipulate physical and mental processes as to bring about events which would have a high improbability of occurrence in ordinary situations.

Such "Grade B" miracles, whether angelic or demonic, however improbable their combinations of circumstances, must still function within the framework of the first and second laws of thermodynamics.

138

"Grade A" miracles, on the other hand, since they require special creation of matter, energy, or complexity, are beyond the reach of Satanic angels altogether (sometimes a demonic mental deception of the individual may make him *think* he is witnessing such a miracle, when in reality he is merely experiencing an illusion). Even God's holy angels, created for the very purpose of serving as "ministering spirits" to those who are the "heirs of salvation" (Hebrews 1:14), can only be instruments in the accomplishment of miracles of creation, as God the Creator ordains, directs and empowers.

Grade B miracles have occurred not only in Biblical times but also all through history, and they still occur frequently today. God answers the prayers of His people, often in what appear to be highly improbable combinations of circumstances. These miracles are not truly supernatural events, however, since they merely represent unusual functioning of *natural* processes, operating within the framework of the first and second laws of thermodynamics.

Miracles of creation, on the other hand, have always been extremely rare events, requiring some highly important reason for God to interfere in the universal natural laws which He himself had ordained. Even in the Bible (except for the continuing creative miracle of Biblical inspiration), Grade A miracles usually occurred only during times of great spiritual crisis (e.g., the Exodus from Egypt, the conquest of Canaan, the deep apostasy during the days of Elijah and Elisha, the ministry of Christ, the apostolic establishment of the church), when it was essential that God validate His Word by direct creative intervention in His world.

Now that the inscripturated Word of God has been completely validated not only by Christ's resurrection but also by 1950 years of His preservation of His Word and His church, there is no reason for Him to capriciously change His laws today. Consequently, any modern alleged miracles of creation should be examined very critically, both scientifically and theologically, before accepting them as authentic.

With one important exception! "Therefore if any man be in Christ, He is a new creation: old things are passed away: behold, all things are become new" (II Corinthians 5:17). The miracle of regeneration, by which the Holy Spirit imparts Christ's eternal life to a new believer, is a grade A miracle that is far beyond the power of any natural process to accomplish, requiring the presence and power of God Himself.

Thermodynamics and Eschatology

If the first and second laws of thermodynamics were to continue functioning as universal laws into the eternal future, the eschatological future would be dismal indeed. Time's Arrow points down, and the cosmos is proceeding inexorably toward an ultimate "thermodynamic death." The sun and all the stars will burn away, and eventually all the available energy of the universe will be unavailable; uniformly low-level heat energy, at the same temperature everywhere, will exist throughout the universe. The universe will (according to the first law) never cease to exist, but it will *die*!

That is, it would die if there were no Creator. The Creator who made it in the first place, and wound it up, and who in fact imposed on it the very decay principle which now seems to predict its death, will yet accomplish all His original purposes — and these do *not* include the un-creation of His creation! Note again the tremendous promise of Romans 8:20–22.

Nevertheless, a traumatic change still awaits the earth. The decay/death principle which now afflicts "the whole creation" is active because of sin, and thus cannot be removed until sin and all its effects have been purged.

The prophetic Scriptures do predict many profound changes scheduled for the earth and the heavens in the days ahead, but these are beyond the scope of this study. They are to be climaxed by a chaotic intensification of the normal decay processes which have operated ever since the curse was pronounced by God on His creation. The Apostle Peter describes it thus:

> "The heavens shall pass away with a great noise, and the elements shall melt with fervent heat, the earth also and the works that are therein shall be burned up.—all these things shall be dissolved—. —the heaven being on fire shall be dissolved, and the elements shall melt with fervent heat"
>
> (II Peter 3:10–12).

This passage has been variously interpreted, but obviously describes a profound and ultimate disintegration of "the heavens and the earth which are now" (II Peter 3:7). The cosmos is not to be annihilated, but it is possible that atomic disintegrations are involved, which will convert mass into heat, sound and other forms of energy. The total mass/energy in the cosmos will be unchanged, so that the first law remains inviolate. The second law also continues to operate, except that rates of disintegration will operate more pervasively and catastrophically than at any time since the world began. The universe did not begin with a "big bang," as evolutionists allege, but its present form will *end* with a big bang (not with a "whimper," as some have predicted), and the cosmos will die its "heat death," — not of old age, but by divine execution.

"Nevertheless, we, according to His promise, look for new heavens and a new earth, wherein dwelleth righteousness" (II Peter 3:13)

After the judgment of God's great white throne (Revelation 20:11–15), God will *create* and make new heavens and a new earth (Isaiah 65:17; 66:22), so that His creative power will once again be exercised throughout the entire universe.

All the age-long effects of sin (e.g., the fossils in the earth's sedimentary crust) will have been purged from the very elements, and there will be "no more curse" (Revelation 22:3). These will be "the times of restoration of all things" (Acts 3:21). The perfect conditions of pristine Eden will be restored, and no doubt vastly enlarged and varied as well. The second law of thermodynamics will be repealed, and "there shall be no more death" (Revelation 21:4) in all the universe, throughout all the ages to come.

REFERENCES

[1] Asimov, Isaac 1970 In the game of energy and thermodynamics you can't even break even. *Smithsonian*. June p. 6.

[2] *Ibid*. p. 8.

[3] *Ibid*. p. 10.

[4] Davies, Paul C. W., 1979 Universe in reverse: can time run backwards? *Second Look* 1:27.

[5] *Ibid*. p. 27.

[6] *Ibid*.